Third Workshop on Automatic Simultaneous Translation Challenges, Recent Advances, and Future Directions (AutoSimTrans 2022)

Online
15 - 16 July 2022

ISBN: 978-1-7138-5623-8

Printed from e-media with permission by:

Curran Associates, Inc.
57 Morehouse Lane
Red Hook, NY 12571

proceedings.com

Some format issues inherent in the e-media version may also appear in this print version.

Association for Computational Linguistics
209 N. Eighth Street
Stroudsburg, Pennsylvania 18360

Phone: 1-570-476-8006
Fax: 1-570-476-0860

acl@aclweb.org

Additional copies of this publication are available from:

Curran Associates, Inc.
57 Morehouse Lane
Red Hook, NY 12571 USA
Phone: 845-758-0400
Fax: 845-758-2633
Email: curran@proceedings.com
Web: www.proceedings.com

AutoSimTrans 2022

Automatic Simultaneous Translation
Challenges, Recent Advances, and Future Directions

The Proceedings of the Third Workshop

July 15-16, 2022

The AutoSimTrans organizers gratefully acknowledge the support from the following sponsors.

Thanks to

Order copies of this and other ACL proceedings from:

Association for Computational Linguistics (ACL)
209 N. Eighth Street
Stroudsburg, PA 18360
USA
Tel: +1-570-476-8006
Fax: +1-570-476-0860
acl@aclweb.org

Introduction

Welcome to the Third Workshop on Automatic Simultaneous Translation (AutoSimTrans)! Simultaneous translation, which performs translation concurrently with the source speech, is widely useful in many scenarios such as international conferences, negotiations, press releases, legal proceedings, and medicine. It combines the AI technologies of machine translation (MT), automatic speech recognition (ASR), and text-to-speech synthesis (TTS) and is rapidly becoming a cutting-edge research field.

As an emerging and interdisciplinary field, simultaneous translation faces many great challenges. This workshop will bring together researchers and practitioners in machine translation, speech processing, and human interpretation, to discuss recent advances and open challenges of simultaneous translation.

We organized a simultaneous translation shared task on Chinese-English and English-Spanish. We released a dataset for open research, which covers speeches in a wide range of domains, such as IT, economy, culture, biology, arts, etc.

Following the tradition of our last two workshops, we will have two sets of keynote speakers: Juan Pino and Trevor Cohn from simultaneous translation, and Weiwei Wang and Wallace Chen from human interpretation research. We hope this workshop will greatly increase the communication and cross-fertilization between the two fields. We have accepted 7 papers that will be presented in the workshop.

We look forward to an exciting workshop.

Hua Wu, Liang Huang, Zhongjun He, Qun Liu, Wolfgang Macherey, and Julia Ive

Organizing Committee

Organizing Committee

Hua Wu, Baidu
Liang Huang, Oregon State University
Zhongjun He, Baidu
Qun Liu, Huawei Noah's Ark Lab
Wolfgang Macherey, Google
Julia Ive, Queen Mary, University of London

Steering Committee

Mark Liberman, University of Pennsylvania
Haifeng Wang, Baidu Inc.

Program Chair

Julia Ive, Queen Mary, University of London

Publicity Chair

Qun Liu, Huawei Noah's Ark Lab

Sponsorship Chair

Wolfgang Macherey, Google

Shared Task Chair

Ruiqing Zhang, Baidu Inc.
Renjie Zheng, Baidu Research

Program Committee

Program Chairs

Hua Wu, Baidu
Liang Huang, Oregon State University
Zhongjun He, Baidu
Qun Liu, Huawei Noah's Ark Lab
Wolfgang Macherey, Google
Julia Ive, Queen Mary, University of London

Keynote Talk: Invited Talk 1

Weiwei Wang
Guangdong University of Foreign Studies

Abstract: Bridging the Gap: CSE-Interpreting Scales as a Measuring Instrument for Interpreting Training
With more than 500 undergraduate and postgraduate degree programs in translation and interpreting (T&I) being launched over the past decade, interpreter training and education has been developing rapidly in China. This creates a huge demand for testing and assessment of interpreting in the educational context. To provide reliable measurement of interpreting competence, the CSE-Interpreting Scales were unveiled in 2018 after 4 years of government-funded research and validation among 30,682 students, 5,787 teachers, and 139 interpreting professionals from 28 provinces, municipalities, and regions in China. In 2022, the scales were developed from conceptual descriptors to an AI-based application to assist in interpreting training. What are the CSE-Interpreting Scales? What are the scenarios and functions of the scales in interpreting training? I will address these questions in my talk by elaborating on two scales and discussing possible applications of the scales in interpreting teaching, learning and assessment.

Bio: Weiwei WANG is an Associate Professor in the School of Interpreting and Translation Studies at Guangdong University of Foreign Studies. Her research focuses on interpreting quality assessment. She is particularly interested in understanding developmental patterns of interpreting competence and causal factors in competence development. Her research has been published widely in peer-reviewed journals. She has led several research projects funded by the Ministry of Education, the National Social Science Foundation, and the British Council. She is serving as the Deputy Secretary-General of the National Interpreting Committee of the Translation Association of China.

Keynote Talk: Invited Talk 2

Wallace Chen
Middlebury Institute of International Studies at Monterey (MIIS)

Abstract: Parsing Techniques in Simultaneous Interpreting and Their Implications for Automatic Simultaneous Translation
Human interpreters employ a wide variety of parsing techniques as dynamic, on-demand strategies to cope with linguistic and communicative challenges associated with simultaneous interpreting (SI). These techniques may include, but not limited to, paraphrasing, generalizing, normalizing, implicitating, explicitating, glossing, shining-through, anticipating, chunking, segmenting, conjoining, etc. – all prompted by the interpreter's level of experience, cognitive load, and a desire to bridge communicative gaps in the interpreting process. While the technology of automatic simultaneous translation relies on a large set of purpose-built training data to construct a coherent translation, human interpreters make calculated and informed decisions, often on a case-by-case basis, when applying the afore-mentioned parsing techniques for SI. This presentation will focus on the somewhat volatile nature of simultaneous interpreting by exploring how and when the various SI techniques are applied, and how they might be able to shed new insights on the development of automatic simultaneous translation systems.

Bio: Wallace Chen is Professor and Program Head of Chinese-English Translation and Interpretation at the Middlebury Institute of International Studies at Monterey (MIIS). He holds an MA in Chinese-English Translation and Interpretation (MIIS) and a Ph.D. in Corpus-Based Translation Studies (University of Manchester, UK). Professor Chen has been teaching Chinese-English translation and interpretation (T&I) since 1997. He has over 30 years of experience in practicing T&I, providing services to major corporations, government agencies, and international organizations spanning across Asia and North America. Professor Chen lectures in a wide variety of T&I areas, including professional skill development, pedagogy, T&I technology, professional assessment, T&I practice, and corpus-based T&I studies.

Keynote Talk: Invited Talk 3

Trevor Cohn
The University of Melbourne

Abstract: From Simultaneous Translation to Simultaneous Interpretation
Simultaneous translation is a highly challenging problem, both for humans and for machines, bringing many additional complexities beyond offline translation. In this talk I will discuss two avenues for advancing research automatic simultaneous translation, encompassing both algorithms and evaluation methodology. First, I will discuss means of improving the realism of models learned from parallel translation data, based on factoring the system into two components: a programmer, which decides when to wait for more input and when to produce translations, and an interpreter, which generates the output tokens. Critically, our method couples the learning of these components, framed as imitation learning, which leads to better simultaneous translation than simply learning a single component, as in prior work. In the second part of the talk, I will revisit a core assumption underlying modern simultaneous translation work, namely the use of parallel offline translation data for evaluation. Instead, I will argue that interpretation data is a better evaluation resource. Interpretation differs substantially from offline translation and includes a range of translation strategies humans to perform this cognitively challenging task in a real-time setting. I will describe a small dataset we curated from the audio and transcripts of European parliament debates. Leading simultaneous translation systems evaluated on this dataset fare quite poorly, relative to standard translation-based evaluation corpora. I will finish by showing how we can adapt existing methods to improve performance on this highly challenging interpretation task.

Bio: Trevor Cohn is a Professor in the School of Computing and Information Systems at The University of Melbourne, and Director of the ARC Training Centre in Cognitive Computing for Medical Technologies. He was previously employed at the University of Sheffield and the University of Edinburgh. His research interests focus on development of probabilistic and statistical machine learning methods for modelling natural language text, with particular focus in machine translation, multilingual model transfer and model robustness to adversarial attacks. He has projects ranging from privacy preserving learning, ameliorating cultural bias from models of language, and natural language understanding of patent documents. He has best paper awards from top tier conferences, including EMNLP and ACL. He served as the Programme Chair of EMNLP, architecting the "Findings" companion publication, and is an action editor for Transactions of the ACL, among other service roles. Trevor completed his PhD in Engineering in 2007 at The University of Melbourne.

Keynote Talk: Invited Talk 4

Juan Pino
Meta AI

Abstract: Recent Advances in Direct Speech to Speech Translation
Speech to speech translation is the task of translating from audio in a language to audio in a different language. Simply combining speech recognition, machine translation and speech synthesis provides a very strong baseline but with some possible drawbacks. We propose to solve the problem in a more direct fashion to potentially provide less error compounding, lower latency and also support translation into unwritten languages or languages without standard writing system. In this presentation, I will describe recent advances on direct speech-to-speech translation, systems with simultaneous capability and that leverage real target speech.

Bio: Juan Pino is a Research Scientist at Meta AI since 2014. He studied machine translation at the University of Cambridge with Professor Bill Byrne. Juan is currently interested in developing end-to-end simultaneous speech translation models.

Table of Contents

Program

Friday, July 15, 2022

07:20 - 07:30 *Opening Remarks*

07:30 - 10:30 *Session 1. Invited Talks and Research Paper*

Over-Generation Cannot Be Rewarded: Length-Adaptive Average Lagging for Simultaneous Speech Translation
Sara Papi, Marco Gaido, Matteo Negri and Marco Turchi

10:30 - 18:30 *Break*

18:30 - 20:10 *Session 2. Shared Task*

Findings of the Third Workshop on Automatic Simultaneous Translation
Ruiqing Zhang, Chuanqiang Zhang, Zhongjun He, Hua Wu, Haifeng Wang, Liang Huang, Qun Liu, Julia Ive and Wolfgang Macherey

BIT-Xiaomi's System for AutoSimTrans 2022
Mengge Liu, Xiang Li, Bao Chen, Yanzhi Tian, Tianwei Lan, Silin Li, Yuhang Guo, Jian Luan and Bin Wang

USST's System for AutoSimTrans 2022
Zhu Jia Hui and Yu Jun

System Description on Automatic Simultaneous Translation Workshop
Zecheng Li, Yue Sun and Haoze Li

System Description on Third Automatic Simultaneous Translation Workshop
Zhang Yiqiao

End-to-End Simultaneous Speech Translation with Pretraining and Distillation: Huawei Noah's System for AutoSimTranS 2022
Xingshan Zeng, Pengfei Li, Liangyou Li and Qun Liu

Findings of the Third Workshop on Automatic Simultaneous Translation

Ruiqing Zhang[1] **Chuanqiang Zhang**[1] **Zhongjun He**[1] **Hua Wu**[1] **Haifeng Wang**[1]
Liang Huang[2] **Qun Liu**[3] **Julia Ive**[4] **Wolfgang Macherey**[5]

[1] Baidu Inc. [2] Oregon State University [3] Huawei Noah's Ark Lab
[4] Queen Mary University of London [5] Google

Abstract

This paper reports the results of the shared task we hosted on the Third Workshop of Automatic Simultaneous Translation (AutoSimTrans). The shared task aims to promote the development of text-to-text and speech-to-text simultaneous translation, and includes Chinese-English and English-Spanish tracks. The number of systems submitted this year has increased fourfold compared with last year. Additionally, the top 1 ranked system in the speech-to-text track is the first end-to-end submission we have received in the past three years, which has shown great potential. This paper reports the results and descriptions of the 14 participating teams, compares different evaluation metrics, and revisits the ranking method.

1 Introduction

Simultaneous translation (ST), which aims to perform translation from source language speech into the target language with high quality and low latency, is widely used in many scenarios, such as international conferences, live broadcasts, etc.

Generally, the research of ST falls into two categories: the cascade method, and the end-to-end method. A typical cascade ST system consists of an automatic speech recognition (ASR) system that transcribes the source speech into streaming text (Moritz et al., 2020; Wang et al., 2020a; Li et al., 2020a), a machine translation (MT) system that translates the text into the target language, and a policy module lies in between them to decide when to start translation (Oda et al., 2014; Dalvi et al., 2018; Ma et al., 2019; Arivazhagan et al., 2019; Zhang et al., 2020; Wilken et al., 2020). Another branch of work proposed end-to-end ST methods that attempt to translate from source speech to target text directly without transcribing the source speech (Bansal et al., 2018; Di Gangi et al., 2019; Jia et al., 2019).

We host a shared task at the Third AutoSimTrans Workshop to promote the exploration of advanced ST approaches. The shared task is built on the past two editions (Wu et al., 2020; Zhang et al., 2021c). We set up three tracks this year:

- **Chinese-English Text-to-text ST track**, where participants are asked to generate real-time English translation based on the input Chinese text. The input is derived from human-annotated transcriptions of TED-like lectures, which contain speech disfluencies but no ASR errors. We simulate streaming speech recognition results by a series of prefixes, where each n-word transcription is represented by n sentence prefixes whose lengths increase from 1 to n.

- **Chinese-English Speech-to-text track** considers real ST scenarios that need real-time translation directly from speech. The participants can adopt either cascade or end-to-end systems. The test sets for the first two tracks are from the same set of audio so that the test results may capture the differences brought by different input modalities.

- **English-Spanish Text-to-text track** is newly added this year. We use the UN Parallel corpus[1] for train and test, which is composed of official records of the United Nations and other parliamentary documents, with no disfluencies and no ASR errors.

The objective of ST systems is to achieve high translation quality with low latency. During the evaluation period, each participant can submit once a day. To examine their quality-latency trade-off ability, the submission of each track is required to contain multiple folders with different policies and varying latency. Our platform supports automatic evaluation and plots the result of each folder to one point on a latency-quality diagram.

[1] https://conferences.unite.un.org/UNCORPUS/en/

Proceedings of the Third Workshop on Automatic Simultaneous Translation, pages 1 - 11
July 15-16, 2022 ©2022 Association for Computational Linguistics

Team	Organization
BIT-Xiaomi	Beijing Institute of Technology & Xiaomi Inc., Beijing, China
Huawei	Huawei Noah's Ark Lab, Guangdong, China
HAU	Huazhong Agricultural University, Hubei, China
USST-ECUST	Univ. of Shanghai for Science and Technology & East China Univ. of Science
HZLHZ	Anonymous
ZXN	Zhejiang Univ. & Xiamen Univ. & North China Institute of Aerospace Engineering
TMU	Tianjin Medical University, Tianjin, China
CITC	Changchun Information Technology College, Jilin, China
NCIAE	North China Institute of Aerospace Engineering, Hebei, China
XJTU	Xi'an Jiaotong University, Shanxi, China
HIT	Harbin Institute of Technology, Heilongjiang, China
ZJU	Zhejiang University, Zhejiang, China
Nuctech	Nuctech Company, Beijing, China
A23	Anonymous

Table 1: List of participants.

We've received 24 submissions from 14 teams this year, 4 times as many as last year. The 14 participants are listed in Table 1. We analyze the submissions and get the following findings:

- The translation quality of the systems, both pipeline and end-to-end in the speech-to-text track lags behind the text-to-text track by more than 9.0 BLEU. This suggests the necessity of exploring robust speech translation systems for pragmatic ST.
- We receive an end-to-end ST submission for the first time in three years, which outperforms all pipeline-based systems submitted this year, representing the potential of end-to-end ST.
- Experiments comparing multiple quality estimation metrics suggest that BLEURT may be more suitable for ST than BLEU given that it correlates best with human ratings.

We will introduce the details of the three tracks (Section 2), report and analyze the submissions (Section 3), and finally compare and analyze evaluation and ranking metrics (Section 4).

2 Shared Task

We first introduce the corpora used in the shared task, then describe the system evaluation method, as well as the differences compared with the past editions.

2.1 Dataset

The corpora provided for training and evaluation are listed in Table 2. For the first two tracks for Zh→En ST, we provide a large-scale text translation corpus, CWMT19[2], along with a speech translation dataset, BSTC (Zhang et al., 2021b). CWMT19 contains 9 million of Zh→En sentence pairs collected from web, bilingual books, movies, law documents, etc. BSTC contains 70.41 hours of Mandarin speeches from three TED-like content producers, corresponding to about 40K source sentences. Compared with last year, we expand the testset of BSTC from 6 talks (1.46 hours) to 20 talks (4.26 hours). For En→Es ST, we use a text translation corpus, the United Nations Parallel Corpus (UN)[3] to simulate the ST scenario. All data can be obtained at the site of our shared task[4] after registration.

The two text-to-text tracks restrict participants to use the provided corpora only, while the speech-to-text track allows the use of additional ASR datasets.

2.2 System Evaluation

The ST systems are evaluated with respect to translation quality and latency. For translation quality, BLEU (Papineni et al., 2002) is the most commonly used metric. Although some net-based approaches such as BERTScore (Zhang et al., 2019) and BLEURT (Sellam et al., 2020) have been

[2] http://mteval.cipsc.org.cn:81/agreement/description

[3] https://conferences.unite.un.org/UNCORPUS/en

[4] https://aistudio.baidu.com/aistudio/competition/detail/148/

	Corpus	Subset	Talks	Utterances	Transcription (words)	Translation (words)	Audio (hours)
Zh-En	BSTC (ST)	Train	215	37,901	1,004,128	620,263	64.57
		Dev	16	956	24,711	15,794	1.58
		Test	20	2,305	72,695	42,836	4.26
	CWMT19 (MT)	Train	/	9,023,456	264,652,945	182,840,035	/
En-Es	UN (MT)	Train	/	21,911,121	517,327,737	608,514,316	/
		Dev	/	500	12,400	14,701	/
		Test	/	500	13,421	15,935	/

Table 2: The summary of our provided corpora. We calculate the number of talks (Talks), number of sentence pairs (Utterances), number of words[5] in transcription and translation, and the duration of the speeches in corresponding corpora.

proven to be superior to BLEU in text translation, little work has conducted experiments or used them to evaluate ST systems. For the evaluation of latency, recent work have proposed some metrics like Average Proportion (AP) (Cho and Esipova, 2016), Average Lagging (AL) (Ma et al., 2019), Consecutive Wait (CW) (Gu et al., 2017) and Differentiable Average Lagging (DAL) (Arivazhagan et al., 2019).

In our shared task this year, we adopt AL-BLEU and CW-BLEU to evaluate systems in the text-to-text tracks and the speech-to-text track, respectively. AL takes the number of words that the target lags behind the source speaker to estimate the degree of delay. It simulates an ideal policy that generates translation at the same speed as the speaker's utterance and measures the average number of words that lags behind this ideal policy. CW measures the average duration between every two WRITE operations by calculating the average number of source words being waited for.

We will conduct experiments and discuss alternative metrics for evaluating translation quality and latency in Section 4.

2.3 Submission and Ranking

Submission: Each team can participate in multiple tracks. Participants in each track are ranked independently. Different from previous editions, the input of the testsets this year is no longer invisible. Participants only need to submit the simultaneous translation results of the testset to our platform, rather than Docker projects. Before the final submission, participants can submit once a day to view their results and those of other teams on the leaderboard. Each submission needs to contain N ($N \geq 1$) folders containing the ST results with different policies or models. The submissions will be evaluated automatically and plotted to N points on the latency-quality graph. N is determined by the teams themselves.

Ranking: Intuitively, a system is considered better if it generates higher quality results under the same delay or achieves a lower delay when generating results of the same quality. In the shared task, we rank submitted systems based on the Iterative Monotonic Optimal Sequence (I-MOS) algorithm (Zhang et al., 2021c). It iteratively searches for a monotonic optimal sequence (MOS), which contains the points with the best translation quality at corresponding delays. Teams that have points selected on the MOS in the kth iteration are classified to the kth level, then removed from the candidate teams in the $k+1^{th}$ iteration. All teams of the kth level rank higher than that of the $k+1^{th}$ level. Teams belonging to the same level are ranked according to the proportion of points on the MOS.

2.4 Differences With Past Editions

In addition to setting up a new En-Es text-to-text ST track, this year's shared task has the following two differences compared with the past editions:

- Participants submit ST results instead of docker projects, which is much easier for participants. For this, we released the audios and corresponding transcription for the first two tracks of Zh-En ST and extended the testset from 6 talks to 20.
- This year's shared task allows each team to submit once per day, rather than only once in the entire challenge period. We developed an automated evaluation platform, enabling participants to access their evaluation results in real-time.

[5]Record the number of characters in the Transcriptions for Chinese.

Rank	Team	Score
1	BIT-Xiaomi	7.00
2	Huawei	6.00
2	USST-ECUST	6.00
4	HZLHZ	4.50
4	HAU	4.50
6	TMU	4.00
7	CITC	3.33
8	NCIAE	3.33
9	ZXN	2.67
10	XJTU	2.00
11	HIT2	1.67
12	ZJU	1.50
13	Nuctech	1.00

Table 3: The ranking of the Zh→En text-to-text ST track. The scores are calculated according to the I-MOS algorithm.

3 System Results

3.1 Chinese-English Simultaneous Translation

The first two tracks are for Chinese-English ST from Chinese text and speech, respectively. We've received submissions from 13 teams: 13 entered the text-to-text track and 4 of them also participated in the speech-to-text track. Their latency-quality trade-off results are plotted in Figure 1.

3.1.1 The Text-to-text track

The ranking of the 13 participants in the Zh→En text-to-text track is shown in Table 3. We list the approaches used by some of the participants as follows:

- **BIT-Xiaomi** (Liu et al., 2022) changed the granularity in wait-k policy (Ma et al., 2019) from Chinese characters to words. They proposed to train a streaming word segmentation model to detect Chinese word boundaries in real-time, and performed prefix-to-prefix training of wait-k according to the number of words. The MT model is a Transformer-big (Vaswani et al., 2017) model trained with data selection, data augmentation (Sennrich et al., 2015), R-drop (Wu et al., 2021), and noise adding strategies to improve the model's robustness.

- **USST-ECUST** (Zhu and Yu, 2022) adopted the Transformer with 12 encoders and 6 decoders as the MT model, which is pre-trained on a large-scale Zh-En corpus containing 9 million sentence pairs from CWMT19 and 5.7 million pairs of pseudo data generated through self-training (He et al., 2019) and back-translation (Sennrich et al., 2015; Edunov et al., 2018). The model is then fine-tuned with prefix-to-prefix training (Ma et al., 2019) on a mixture of BSTC corpus and a subset of CWMT19 that is most similar to BSTC for better domain adaptation.

- **HAU** (Zhang, 2022) trained a prefix-to-prefix model using the wait-k policy with $k = 1$ and 3 in the text-to-text simultaneous translation.

Rank	Team	Score
1	Huawei	2.00
2	BIT-Xiaomi	1.50
3	ZXN	1.00
3	HAU	1.00

Table 4: The ranking of the Zh→En speech-to-text ST track.

3.1.2 The Speech-to-text track

The ranking of the 4 participants in the Zh→En speech-to-text track is listed in Table 4.

- **Huawei** (Zeng et al., 2022) built an end-to-end simultaneous translation model based on RealTranS (Zeng et al., 2021). It includes a CTC-guided acoustic encoder, a semantic encoder, and a translation decoder. The acoustic encoder is initialized from a pre-trained ASR model, and the semantic encoder and the translation decoder are initialized from a pre-trained NMT model. In the fine-tuning stage, they first generated pseudo ST training data by translating the transcripts of 20,000 hours of in-house ASR corpora into the target text, then train the model with the multi-path wait-k (Elbayad et al., 2019) policy on the pseudo data together with BSTC.

- **BIT-Xiaomi** (Liu et al., 2022) took a pipeline system. The audio inputs are firstly segmented by Silero-VAD (Team, 2021), then sent to a Transformer-based ASR model trained on AISHELL-1 (Bu et al., 2017) and BSTC (Zhang et al., 2021b). The recognized text is then sent to the policy model and the MT model to decide when to translate and produce a translation. The MT model and the

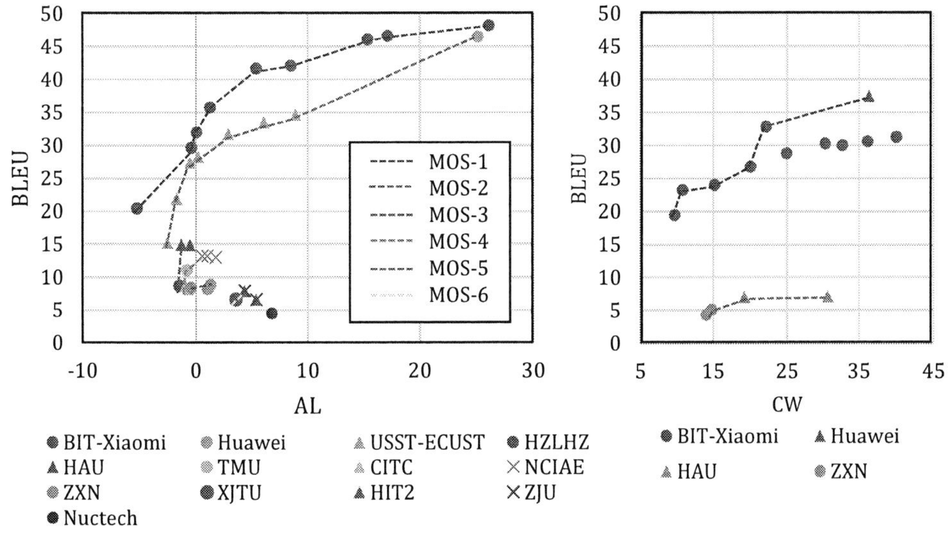

(a). Zh-En Text-to-text ST track (b). Zh-En Speech-to-text ST track

Figure 1: The evaluation results of the first two tracks. The order in the legend (line by line) denotes the ranking result, which is calculated by the I-MOS algorithm. It iteratively builds the monotonic optimal sequence (MOS) of level k (MOS-k) and classifies teams that have points on it to the kth level. We use points of the same color but different shapes to represent the results of teams belonging to the same level, and the teams are ranked according to the proportion of points on the corresponding MOS.

policy module are the same as they used in the text-to-text track.

- **ZXN** (Li et al., 2022) developed a pipeline system with an audio segmentation model, an ASR system, and a wait-k based MT model. The audio segmentation model performs endpoint detection (EPD) based on short-term energy and zero-crossing rate (Rabiner and Sambur, 1975). The ASR system includes a convolutional model with a CTC decoder (Graves et al., 2006) to generate pinyin sequences, followed by a language model based on the maximum entropy markov model (MEMM) to produce Chinese characters. The MT model adopts Transformer-base (Vaswani et al., 2017) and is trained with the prefix-to-prefix mode. The ASR model is pre-trained on AISHELL-1 and Thchs-30 (Wang and Zhang, 2015), and the MT model is pre-trained on CWMT19, then both are fine-tuned on the BSTC.

- **HAU** (Zhang, 2022) also took a pipeline system. They adopted DeepSpeech2 (Amodei et al., 2016) as the ASR model, which is trained on AISHELL-1 only without further fine-tuning on BSTC. The ST policy and the MT model they used are the same as they used in the text-to-text track.

	Text-to-text	Speech-to-text
BIT-Xiaomi	48.17	31.26
Huawei	46.49	37.46

Table 5: The highest BLEU scores achieved by BIT-Xiaomi and Huawei for the same testset with different input modalities. The Speech-to-text track inputs audios while the Text-to-text track inputs golden transcription.

Table 5 lists the highest translation quality achieved by BIT-Xiaomi and Huawei, the two best performing teams on the two tracks. Compared to their performance on the text-to-text track, their speech-to-text systems both have a BLEU degradation of over 9 points. This quality gap is brought about by different input modalities. The speech-to-text systems receive audio as input, so they need an ASR model to transcribe the audio, or an end-to-end speech translation model to generate translation directly from speech. The pipeline systems have the problem of error propagation, and the performance of the end-to-end systems is limited by data scarcity.

This also gives us some hints that the processing of speech may be the most significant factor

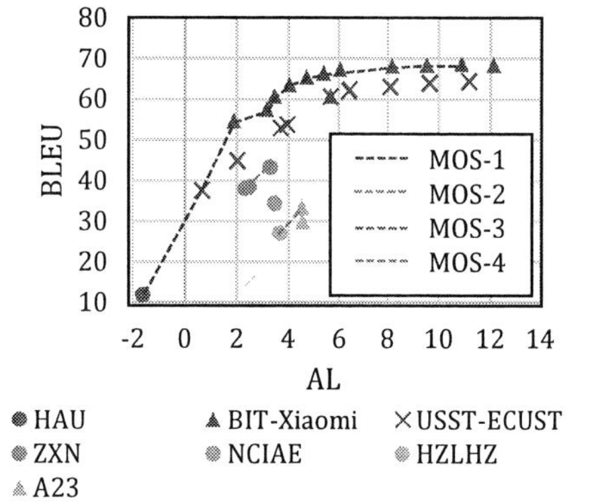

Figure 2: The evaluation results of the En-Es text-to-text ST track.

Rank	Team	Score
1	HAU	4.00
2	BIT-Xiaomi	3.83
3	USST-ECUST	3.08
4	ZXN	3.00
5	NCIAE	2.00
6	HZLHZ	1.00
7	A23	0.50

Table 6: The ranking of the En→Es text-to-text ST track.

affecting the effect of simultaneous translation in real scenes. Some work has attempted to improve the pipeline systems by introducing an ASR error correction model (Leng et al., 2021; Zhang et al., 2021a), others proposed pre-training approaches to alleviate the data scarcity problem of speech translation corpora in end-to-end systems (Wang et al., 2020b; Pino et al., 2020; Zheng et al., 2021; Li et al., 2020b; Zhang et al., 2022). We hope to see more participants in future workshops investigating how to close the performance gap between the two tracks.

3.2 English-Spanish Simultaneous Translation

The En→Es track received submissions from 7 teams. The latency-quality trade-off results of the En-Es track are plotted in Figure 2 and the ranking is listed in Table 6. According to the system descriptions submitted, almost all teams used the same training policies in this track as in the Zh→En text-to-text track.

4 Discussion

We first carry out experiments to compare different translation quality evaluation metrics (Section 4.1), then discuss a controversial ranking dilemma of I-MOS algorithm in the ranking algorithm (Section 4.2).

4.1 BLEU, BERTScore, and BLEURT

	Metrics	$r(\uparrow)$	$\rho(\uparrow)$	$\tau(\uparrow)$
SYS1	SentBLEU	0.546	0.484	0.390
	BERTScore	0.553	0.484	0.388
	BLEURT	**0.708**	**0.655**	**0.537**
SYS2	SentBLEU	0.584	0.516	0.415
	BERTScore	0.587	0.540	0.433
	BLEURT	**0.729**	**0.693**	**0.568**
SYS3	SentBLEU	0.525	0.468	0.374
	BERTScore	0.529	0.498	0.396
	BLEURT	**0.670**	**0.654**	**0.532**
SYS4	SentBLEU	0.467	0.408	0.322
	BERTScore	0.135[6]	0.467	0.368
	BLEURT	**0.637**	**0.629**	**0.507**
SYS5	SentBLEU	0.451	0.422	0.332
	BERTScore	0.518	0.522	0.414
	BLEURT	**0.656**	**0.672**	**0.539**
SYS6	SentBLEU	0.370	0.350	0.274
	BERTScore	0.475	0.480	0.376
	BLEURT	**0.559**	**0.578**	**0.459**

Table 7: Sentence-level agreement with human ratings on 6 ST systems. Given 6 source documents, each system (SYSi) performs ST, and the translation results are evaluated by sentenceBLEU (sentBLEU), BertScore, and BLEURT with 4 references. We calculate the Pearson correlation (r), the Spearman correlation (ρ), and the Kendall Tau (τ) score between the automatic metrics and human ratings. BLEURT has obvious advantages over the other two metrics in all the 6 systems.

Recently, many quality estimation metrics have been proposed to better imitate human evaluation (Specia et al., 2021), such as *RUSE* (Shimanaka et al., 2018), *YiSi* (Mathur et al., 2019), *BERTScore* (Zhang et al., 2019), *BLEURT* (Sellam et al., 2020), etc. These metrics are proven to be superior to traditional quality evaluation metrics like *BLEU* (Papineni et al., 2002) in text translation. However, to the best of our knowledge, no work has conducted experiments in the ST scenario, and almost all ST work still takes *BLEU* as the criterion for translation quality evaluation.

To keep consistent with previous work, we still

[6]This outlier is caused by a missing translation (one sentence generates an empty translation). Different from BERTScore, SentBLEU and BLEURT are less influenced because the BERTscores are relatively high (always higher than 0.9), for which one zero brought by empty translation would largely degrade its Pearson correlation score.

used the document-level BLEU[7] for evaluation in the shared task this year. Now we conduct experiments to compare it with sentence-level BLEU, BERTScore[8], and BLEURT[9].

4.1.1 Agreement between automatic metrics and human ratings

To evaluate the SOTA quality estimation metrics, we ask human annotators to assess the results of multiple ST systems and calculate the agreement between automatic metrics and human ratings. Each sentence is rated to 1, 2, or 3. 1 denotes the translation is inconsistent with the original text, or incomprehensible; 2 denotes the translation conveys the main idea of the original text but with minor mistakes in grammar or word usage; 3 denotes the translation is fully consistent with the original text. In order to ensure uniform rating standard, all evaluated sentences are scored by one annotator first, and then checked by another annotator. The two annotators are both translators who graduated from Chinese-English translation major.

We randomly select 6 documents (including 975 source sentences in total) from the testset of the first track for evaluation, and then select 6 ST systems with high BLEU scores on this testset (SYS1: 30.23, SYS2: 30.35, SYS3: 29.38, SYS4: 33.45, SYS5: 42.05, SYS6: 41.27) and have they manually rated. Given the simultaneous translation result produced by 6 systems, we calculate the Pearson correlation (r), the Spearman correlation (ρ), and the Kendall Tau (τ) points between human ratings and scores of different automatic metrics. As shown in Table 7, *BLEURT* has a higher correlation with human ratings compared with the other two metrics in all the 6 systems.

4.1.2 Using different metrics for ranking

Next, we explore these metrics from the perspective of ranking. Taking the average score of all the evaluated sentences as the ranking basis, we wonder whether each metric would yield a ranking consistent with human evaluations. We first count the proportion of sentences with a human rating of 2 or 3 as the acceptability for each system. Figure 3 shows that the rank (horizontal axis) of the six systems in terms of acceptability, from low to high is: SYS1 < SYS2 < SYS3 < SYS4 < SYS5 < SYS6. Comparing the human-rated acceptability scores and the quality estimated by automatic metrics, we find that Document-level BLEU (*DocBLEU*) and Sentence-level BLEU (*sentBLEU*) score SYS3 inferior to SYS2, *BERTScore* rates SYS2 inferior to SYS1, and all the three metrics rank SYS6 inferior to SYS5. The ranking results of all the three metrics are different from those given by the human-rated acceptability. On the contrary, *BLEURT*'s ranking for the 6 systems is consistent with the human results, indicating its higher accuracy in imitating human judgment. Note that, *BERTScore* rates all systems around 0.98, with no significant differences. This might be caused by the collapse problem (Chen and He, 2021; Yan et al., 2021), meaning that BERT-derived representations are somehow collapsed, so that almost all sentences are mapped to a similar representation and produce high similarity.

Table 8 further lists the correlation between the automatic metrics and human acceptability for the 6

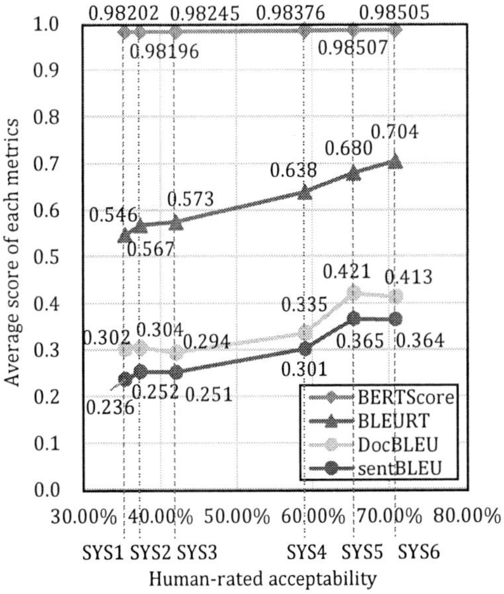

Figure 3: Human-rated acceptability vs. automatic metrics for the translation of 6 systems.

Metrics	$r(\uparrow)$	$\rho(\uparrow)$	$\tau(\uparrow)$
DocBLEU	0.917	0.771	0.600
SentBLEU	0.970	0.886	0.733
BERTScore	0.968	0.886	0.733
BLEURT	**0.994**	**1.000**	**1.000**

Table 8: Document-level agreement with human ratings.

[7]https://github.com/moses-smt/mosesdecoder/blob/master/scripts/generic/mteval-v13a.pl

[8]https://github.com/Tiiiger/bert_score based on roberta-large

[9]https://github.com/google-research/bleurt with BLEURT-20

	Metrics	$r(\uparrow)$	$\rho(\uparrow)$	$\tau(\uparrow)$
SYS3	BLEURT	0.642	0.604	**0.528**
	+ft	**0.654**	**0.620**	0.502
SYS5	BLEURT	0.590	0.597	0.484
	+ft	**0.703**	**0.704**	**0.569**
SYS6	BLEURT	0.526	0.544	0.439
	+ft	**0.639**	**0.643**	**0.516**

Table 9: The correlation between human ratings and BLEURT scores, before and after fine-tuning.

systems, demonstrating the superiority of *BLEURT* to all the other three metrics.

4.1.3 Fine-tuning *BLEURT* on human annotations

We further attempt to improve the performance of *BLEURT* by fine-tuning on some human ratings. We first construct a quality estimation training set consisting of $975 \times 3 \times 4 = 11700$ triples <hypo, ref, score> built by pairing the ST results (hypo) and human ratings (score) of three systems (SYS1, SYS2, and SYS4) with corresponding 4 references (ref). Then we fine-tune *BLEURT* on this training set and evaluate its performance on the remaining three systems. Here we use *BLEURT-Base*[10] for faster training.

The improvements brought by fine-tuning is shown in Table 9. After fine-tuning, the correlation of almost all systems has been significantly improved, especially for SYS5 and SYS6.

4.2 The ranking dilemma

In the shared task, we take the I-MOS algorithm for ranking. It iteratively builds a monotonic optimal sequence (MOS) and considers the proportion of optimal points as the ranking basis. On the quality-latency figure, the MOS is a sequence of optimal points with increasing translation quality and latency, and a point is considered optimal if there is no other point or line above it at an identical latency. Although I-MOS is adaptive to uncertain submission results, it has one drawback, that is, the MOS curve is bound to select the leftmost point regardless of its translation quality, because the leftmost point is definitely an optimal point. Therefore, I-MOS somehow encourages participants to submit only one point with extremely low latency, making the team ranked first place by the I-MOS algorithm, the leftmost point of Figure 2 is such a case.

[10] https://storage.googleapis.com/bleurt-oss/bleurt-base-128.zip

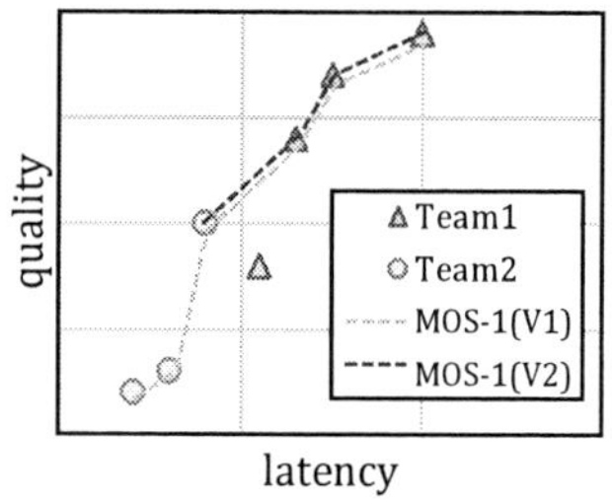

Figure 4: An example to illustrate the ranking dilemma of the I-MOS ranking algorithm. The vanilla I-MOS algorithm calculates MOS-1 as the yellow dotted curve (V1). According to V1, Team2 would rank higher than Team1, although its left two points are unconvincing because of their extremely low quality. After applying our proposed remedy, the left two points of Team2 are removed and Team1 ranks higher based on the modified MOS-1(V2).

To eliminate the defect of I-MOS, we propose to add two strategies to future shared tasks:

1. We require each team to submit at least two points with different delays to make a latency-quality trade-off.

2. Before running the I-MOS algorithm, we first scan to remove the leftmost points whose quality is worse than others' submissions. If all submission points of a team are removed, the team will be ranked last.

   See Figure 4 for example. The vanilla I-MOS algorithm would generate the dashed curve as MOS-1 (V1), causing Team2 to rank higher (Team1 scores $3/4$, Team2 scores $3/3$), although its left two points are unconvincing due to their extremely low quality. But after applying this strategy, we will remove the two points of Team2 because no other team has points with inferior quality compared to them. Then Team2 will be scored to $1/3$. We don't have to worry whether this strategy will lead to unfairness if Team2 is designed for ST at low latency. If Team2 doesn't deliberately take advantage of the defect of I-MOS, they should submit more results at higher latency, at least submit their full-sentence translation result.

5 Conclusion and Future work

This paper presents the results of the simultaneous translation shared task we hosted at the 3rd Workshop on Automatic Simultaneous Translation workshop. The shared task includes three tracks, two text-to-text tracks in different languages, and one speech-to-text track. We analyze the submissions from 14 participating teams and have the following inspirations for future ST work:

1. **Robust ST model**: The results of the first two tracks reveal there exists a great gap between using speech input and its corresponding golden transcriptions. Therefore, it is important to explore robust speech translation systems in real ST scenes.

2. **End-to-end ST**: In the speech-to-text track, we received an end-to-end ST submission system for the first time in three years. It integrates a read-write policy into an end-to-end speech translation model and outperforms all the cascaded systems, representing the potential of end-to-end simultaneous translation models.

3. **Quality Evaluation**: Although recently proposed neural network-based metrics are proven superior to BLEU for standard text translation, ST work always takes BLEU for quality estimation. We compare multiple metrics under the ST scenario and verify that BLEURT is more suitable than BLEU for ST in terms of correlation with human ratings.

4. **System Evaluation**: We propose the I-MOS algorithm as well as its revised version for system ranking. Considering both quality and latency is crucial for a practical ST system. However, the quality-latency metric for ST systems is rarely studied. We suggest further study on this topic.

In future shared tasks, we will make the following changes:

1. **Submission**: Add a requirement that each submission should contain at least two points with different delays to make a latency-quality trade-off.

2. **Criterion**: Use BLEURT to replace BLEU for its better correlation with human ratings.

3. **Ranking**: Removing the leftmost points whose quality is worse than others' submission before running the I-MOS algorithm.

References

Dario Amodei, Sundaram Ananthanarayanan, Rishita Anubhai, Jingliang Bai, Eric Battenberg, Carl Case, Jared Casper, Bryan Catanzaro, Qiang Cheng, Guoliang Chen, et al. 2016. Deep speech 2: End-to-end speech recognition in english and mandarin. In *International conference on machine learning*, pages 173–182. PMLR.

Naveen Arivazhagan, Colin Cherry, Wolfgang Macherey, Chung-Cheng Chiu, Semih Yavuz, Ruoming Pang, Wei Li, and Colin Raffel. 2019. Monotonic infinite lookback attention for simultaneous machine translation. In *Proceedings of the 57th Annual Meeting of the Association for Computational Linguistics*, pages 1313–1323, Florence, Italy. Association for Computational Linguistics.

Sameer Bansal, Herman Kamper, Karen Livescu, Adam Lopez, and Sharon Goldwater. 2018. Pre-training on high-resource speech recognition improves low-resource speech-to-text translation.

Hui Bu, Jiayu Du, Xingyu Na, Bengu Wu, and Hao Zheng. 2017. Aishell-1: An open-source mandarin speech corpus and a speech recognition baseline. In *2017 20th Conference of the Oriental Chapter of the International Coordinating Committee on Speech Databases and Speech I/O Systems and Assessment (O-COCOSDA)*, pages 1–5. IEEE.

Xinlei Chen and Kaiming He. 2021. Exploring simple siamese representation learning. In *Proceedings of the IEEE/CVF Conference on Computer Vision and Pattern Recognition*, pages 15750–15758.

Kyunghyun Cho and Masha Esipova. 2016. Can neural machine translation do simultaneous translation? *arXiv preprint arXiv:1606.02012*.

Fahim Dalvi, Nadir Durrani, Hassan Sajjad, and Stephan Vogel. 2018. Incremental decoding and training methods for simultaneous translation in neural machine translation. In *Proceedings of the 2018 Conference of the North American Chapter of the Association for Computational Linguistics: Human Language Technologies, Volume 2 (Short Papers)*, pages 493–499, New Orleans, Louisiana. Association for Computational Linguistics.

Mattia Antonino Di Gangi, Matteo Negri, Roldano Cattoni, Dessi Roberto, and Marco Turchi. 2019. Enhancing transformer for end-to-end speech-to-text translation. In *Machine Translation Summit XVII*, pages 21–31. European Association for Machine Translation.

Sergey Edunov, Myle Ott, Michael Auli, and David Grangier. 2018. Understanding back-translation at scale. *arXiv preprint arXiv:1808.09381*.

Maha Elbayad, Laurent Besacier, and Jakob Verbeek. 2019. Efficient wait-k models for simultaneous machine translation. In *Interspeech*.

Alex Graves, Santiago Fernández, Faustino Gomez, and Jürgen Schmidhuber. 2006. Connectionist temporal classification: labelling unsegmented sequence data with recurrent neural networks. In *Proceedings of the 23rd international conference on Machine learning*, pages 369–376.

Jiatao Gu, Graham Neubig, Kyunghyun Cho, and Victor OK Li. 2017. Learning to translate in real-time with neural machine translation. In *Proceedings of the 15th Conference of the European Chapter of the Association for Computational Linguistics: Volume 1, Long Papers*, pages 1053–1062.

Junxian He, Jiatao Gu, Jiajun Shen, and Marc'Aurelio Ranzato. 2019. Revisiting self-training for neural sequence generation. *arXiv preprint arXiv:1909.13788*.

Ye Jia, Melvin Johnson, Wolfgang Macherey, Ron J Weiss, Yuan Cao, Chung-Cheng Chiu, Naveen Ari, Stella Laurenzo, and Yonghui Wu. 2019. Leveraging weakly supervised data to improve end-to-end speech-to-text translation. In *ICASSP 2019-2019 IEEE International Conference on Acoustics, Speech and Signal Processing (ICASSP)*, pages 7180–7184. IEEE.

Yichong Leng, Xu Tan, Rui Wang, Linchen Zhu, Jin Xu, Wenjie Liu, Linquan Liu, Tao Qin, Xiang-Yang Li, Edward Lin, et al. 2021. Fastcorrect 2: Fast error correction on multiple candidates for automatic speech recognition. *arXiv preprint arXiv:2109.14420*.

Bo Li, Shuo-yiin Chang, Tara N Sainath, Ruoming Pang, Yanzhang He, Trevor Strohman, and Yonghui Wu. 2020a. Towards fast and accurate streaming end-to-end asr. In *ICASSP 2020-2020 IEEE International Conference on Acoustics, Speech and Signal Processing (ICASSP)*, pages 6069–6073. IEEE.

Xian Li, Changhan Wang, Yun Tang, Chau Tran, Yuqing Tang, Juan Pino, Alexei Baevski, Alexis Conneau, and Michael Auli. 2020b. Multilingual speech translation with efficient finetuning of pretrained models. *arXiv preprint arXiv:2010.12829*.

Zecheng Li, Yue Sun, and Haoze Li. 2022. System description on automatic simultaneous translation workshop. In *The 3rd Workshop on Automatic Simultaneous Translation at NAACL 2022*.

Mengge Liu, Xiang Li, Bao Chen, Yanzhi Tian, Tianwei Lan, Silin Li, Yuhang Guo, Jian Luan, and Bin Wang. 2022. BIT-xiaomi's system for autosimtrans 2022. In *The 3rd Workshop on Automatic Simultaneous Translation at NAACL 2022*.

Mingbo Ma, Liang Huang, Hao Xiong, Kaibo Liu, Chuanqiang Zhang, Zhongjun He, Hairong Liu, Xing Li, and Haifeng Wang. 2019. STACL: simultaneous translation with integrated anticipation and controllable latency. In *ACL 2019*, volume abs/1810.08398.

Nitika Mathur, Timothy Baldwin, and Trevor Cohn. 2019. Putting evaluation in context: Contextual embeddings improve machine translation evaluation. In *Proceedings of the 57th Annual Meeting of the Association for Computational Linguistics*, pages 2799–2808.

Niko Moritz, Takaaki Hori, and Jonathan Le. 2020. Streaming automatic speech recognition with the transformer model. In *ICASSP 2020-2020 IEEE International Conference on Acoustics, Speech and Signal Processing (ICASSP)*, pages 6074–6078. IEEE.

Yusuke Oda, Graham Neubig, Sakriani Sakti, Tomoki Toda, and Satoshi Nakamura. 2014. Optimizing segmentation strategies for simultaneous speech translation. In *Proceedings of the 52nd Annual Meeting of the Association for Computational Linguistics (Volume 2: Short Papers)*, volume 2, pages 551–556.

Kishore Papineni, Salim Roukos, Todd Ward, and Wei-Jing Zhu. 2002. Bleu: a method for automatic evaluation of machine translation. In *Proceedings of the 40th annual meeting on association for computational linguistics*, pages 311–318. Association for Computational Linguistics.

Juan Pino, Qiantong Xu, Xutai Ma, Mohammad Javad Dousti, and Yun Tang. 2020. Self-training for end-to-end speech translation. *arXiv preprint arXiv:2006.02490*.

Lawrence R Rabiner and Marvin R Sambur. 1975. An algorithm for determining the endpoints of isolated utterances. *Bell System Technical Journal*, 54(2):297–315.

Thibault Sellam, Dipanjan Das, and Ankur P Parikh. 2020. Bleurt: Learning robust metrics for text generation. *arXiv preprint arXiv:2004.04696*.

Rico Sennrich, Barry Haddow, and Alexandra Birch. 2015. Improving neural machine translation models with monolingual data. *arXiv preprint arXiv:1511.06709*.

Hiroki Shimanaka, Tomoyuki Kajiwara, and Mamoru Komachi. 2018. Ruse: Regressor using sentence embeddings for automatic machine translation evaluation. In *Proceedings of the Third Conference on Machine Translation: Shared Task Papers*, pages 751–758.

Lucia Specia, Frédéric Blain, Marina Fomicheva, Chrysoula Zerva, Zhenhao Li, Vishrav Chaudhary, and André Martins. 2021. Findings of the wmt 2021 shared task on quality estimation. Association for Computational Linguistics.

Silero Team. 2021. Silero vad: pre-trained enterprise-grade voice activity detector (vad), number detector and language classifier.

Ashish Vaswani, Noam Shazeer, Niki Parmar, Jakob Uszkoreit, Llion Jones, Aidan N Gomez, Łukasz Kaiser, and Illia Polosukhin. 2017. Attention is all you need. In *Advances in Neural Information Processing Systems*, pages 6000–6010.

Chengyi Wang, Yu Wu, Shujie Liu, Jinyu Li, Liang Lu, Guoli Ye, and Ming Zhou. 2020a. Low latency end-to-end streaming speech recognition with a scout network. *arXiv preprint arXiv:2003.10369*.

Chengyi Wang, Yu Wu, Shujie Liu, Zhenglu Yang, and Ming Zhou. 2020b. Bridging the gap between pre-training and fine-tuning for end-to-end speech translation. In *Proceedings of the AAAI Conference on Artificial Intelligence*, volume 34, pages 9161–9168.

Dong Wang and Xuewei Zhang. 2015. Thchs-30: A free chinese speech corpus. *arXiv preprint arXiv:1512.01882*.

Patrick Wilken, Tamer Alkhouli, Evgeny Matusov, and Pavel Golik. 2020. Neural simultaneous speech translation using alignment-based chunking. In *Proceedings of the 17th International Conference on Spoken Language Translation*, pages 237–246, Online. Association for Computational Linguistics.

Hua Wu, Collin Cherry, Liang Huang, Zhongjun He, Mark Liberman, James Cross, and Yang Liu, editors. 2020. *Proceedings of the First Workshop on Automatic Simultaneous Translation*. Association for Computational Linguistics, Seattle, Washington.

Lijun Wu, Juntao Li, Yue Wang, Qi Meng, Tao Qin, Wei Chen, Min Zhang, Tie-Yan Liu, et al. 2021. R-drop: regularized dropout for neural networks. *Advances in Neural Information Processing Systems*, 34.

Yuanmeng Yan, Rumei Li, Sirui Wang, Fuzheng Zhang, Wei Wu, and Weiran Xu. 2021. Consert: A contrastive framework for self-supervised sentence representation transfer. *arXiv preprint arXiv:2105.11741*.

Xingshan Zeng, Liangyou Li, and Qun Liu. 2021. Realtrans: End-to-end simultaneous speech translation with convolutional weighted-shrinking transformer. *arXiv preprint arXiv:2106.04833*.

Xingshan Zeng, Pengfei Li, Liangyou Li, and Qun Liu. 2022. End-to-end simultaneous speech translation with pretraining and distillation: Huawei noah's system for autosimtrans 2022. In *The 3rd Workshop on Automatic Simultaneous Translation at NAACL 2022*.

Ruiqing Zhang, Zhongjun He, Hua Wu, and Haifeng Wang. 2022. Learning adaptive segmentation policy for end-to-end simultaneous translation. In *Proceedings of the 60th Annual Meeting of the Association for Computational Linguistics (Volume 1: Long Papers)*, pages 7862–7874, Dublin, Ireland. Association for Computational Linguistics.

Ruiqing Zhang, Chao Pang, Chuanqiang Zhang, Shuohuan Wang, Zhongjun He, Yu Sun, Hua Wu, and Haifeng Wang. 2021a. Correcting Chinese spelling errors with phonetic pre-training. In *Findings of the Association for Computational Linguistics: ACL-IJCNLP 2021*, pages 2250–2261, Online. Association for Computational Linguistics.

Ruiqing Zhang, Xiyang Wang, Chuanqiang Zhang, Zhongjun He, Hua Wu, Zhi Li, Haifeng Wang, Ying Chen, and Qinfei Li. 2021b. BSTC: A large-scale Chinese-English speech translation dataset. In *Proceedings of the Second Workshop on Automatic Simultaneous Translation*, pages 28–35, Online. Association for Computational Linguistics.

Ruiqing Zhang, Chuanqiang Zhang, Zhongjun He, Hua Wu, and Haifeng Wang. 2020. Learning adaptive segmentation policy for simultaneous translation. In *Proceedings of the 2020 Conference on Empirical Methods in Natural Language Processing (EMNLP)*, pages 2280–2289.

Ruiqing Zhang, Chuanqiang Zhang, Zhongjun He, Hua Wu, and Haifeng Wang. 2021c. Findings of the second workshop on automatic simultaneous translation. In *Proceedings of the Second Workshop on Automatic Simultaneous Translation*, pages 36–44, Online. Association for Computational Linguistics.

Tianyi Zhang, Varsha Kishore, Felix Wu, Kilian Q Weinberger, and Yoav Artzi. 2019. Bertscore: Evaluating text generation with bert. *arXiv preprint arXiv:1904.09675*.

Yiqiao Zhang. 2022. System description on third automatic simultaneous translation workshop. In *The 3rd Workshop on Automatic Simultaneous Translation at NAACL 2022*.

Renjie Zheng, Junkun Chen, Mingbo Ma, and Liang Huang. 2021. Fused acoustic and text encoding for multimodal bilingual pretraining and speech translation. In *International Conference on Machine Learning*, pages 12736–12746. PMLR.

JiaHui Zhu and Jun Yu. 2022. USST's system for autosimtrans 2022. In *The 3rd Workshop on Automatic Simultaneous Translation at NAACL 2022*.

Over-Generation Cannot Be Rewarded: Length-Adaptive Average Lagging for Simultaneous Speech Translation

Sara Papi[◇,△], **Marco Gaido**[◇,△], **Matteo Negri**[◇], **Marco Turchi**[◇]
[◇]Fondazione Bruno Kessler
[△]University of Trento
{spapi, mgaido, negri, turchi}@fbk.eu

Abstract

Simultaneous speech translation (SimulST) systems aim at generating their output with the lowest possible latency, which is normally computed in terms of Average Lagging (AL). In this paper we highlight that, despite its widespread adoption, AL provides underestimated scores for systems that generate longer predictions compared to the corresponding references. We also show that this problem has practical relevance, as recent SimulST systems have indeed a tendency to over-generate. As a solution, we propose LAAL (Length-Adaptive Average Lagging), a modified version of the metric that takes into account the over-generation phenomenon and allows for unbiased evaluation of both under-/over-generating systems.

1 Introduction

Simultaneous speech-to-text translation (SimulST) is the task in which the generation of the textual translation in the target language starts before the entire audio input in the source language has been ingested by the model. The need to have high quality translations in the shortest possible time therefore becomes the main objective of SimulST systems, which have to satisfy specific time requirements depending on the application scenarios. These requirements are usually expressed in terms of latency, that is the elapsed time between the pronunciation of a word and the generation of its textual translation. How latency is measured hence plays a crucial role in systems evaluation.

The SimulST task was initially addressed using cascaded models (Fügen et al., 2007; Oda et al., 2014) that divide the translation process into two steps: simultaneous automatic speech recognition (Jaitly et al., 2016; Rao et al., 2017), and simultaneous machine translation (Cho and Esipova, 2016; Gu et al., 2017). For this reason, the first latency metrics were designed to evaluate simultaneous machine translation (SimulMT) systems (Cho and Esipova, 2016; Cherry and Foster, 2019; Elbayad et al., 2020). Among them, Average Lagging – AL – (Ma et al., 2019) is the most popular one, and its adaptation to SimulST by Ma et al. (2020a) has become a widely adopted (Ma et al., 2020b; Zeng et al., 2021; Chen et al., 2021; Liu et al., 2021) *de facto* standard.[1] The adaptation by Ma et al. (2020a) sparks from a weakness observed in the original formulation of the metric. Being susceptible to *under-generation*, it results in biased evaluations favouring systems that produce shorter predictions compared to the reference. However, though successful in correcting this behaviour, the proposed adaptation did not consider the opposite case of *over-generation*, which occurs when the prediction is longer than the reference.

To fill this gap, in this paper we introduce LAAL (Length-Adaptive Average Lagging):[2] a simple yet effective extension of AL that takes into account also over-generation and allows for fair SimulST systems comparisons. After a brief explanation of AL calculation (Section 2), we expose its incorrect behaviour in presence of over-generation phenomena (Section 3) and show that over-generation is actually present in the output of recent SimulST systems (Section 4). Then, we present the new LAAL metric (Section 5), whose computation is adjusted at sentence level by looking at the length of model predictions. Through examples, we show that, unlike the previous AL formulation, our metric is able to fairly evaluate both under- and over-generating systems. We conclude our work with a discussion (Section 6) about problems that still need to be solved for latency computation, remarking that our proposal represents a first step toward a more reliable assessment of SimulST systems

[1]For instance, the IWSLT SimulST Shared Task (Anastasopoulos et al., 2021) relies on AL to divide the systems in different latency regimes (low, medium, high) and BLEU (Post, 2018) to rank the them based on translation quality.

[2]The code is available at: `https://github.com/hlt-mt/FBK-fairseq`.

Proceedings of the Third Workshop on Automatic Simultaneous Translation, pages 12 - 17
July 15-16, 2022

performance.

2 Average Lagging

The idea behind the AL metric is to quantify how much time the system is out of sync with the speaker. In SimulST, the input sequence is represented as a stream of audio speech in the source language $\mathbf{X} = [x_1, ..., x_{|\mathbf{X}|}]$ where each element x_j is a raw audio segment of duration T_j, the reference as a stream of words in the target language $\mathbf{Y}^* = [y_1^*, ..., y_{|\mathbf{Y}^*|}^*]$, and the model translation as a stream of predicted words $\mathbf{Y} = [y_1, ..., y_{|\mathbf{Y}|}]$. In the simultaneous setting, a system starts to generate a partial hypothesis while it continues to receive an incremental stream of input. This implies that, to generate the y_i target word at time j, it has access to $\mathbf{X}_{1:j} = [x_1, ..., x_j]$ with $j < |\mathbf{X}|$.

Therefore, the delay with which the y_i word is emitted is $d_i = \sum_{i=1}^{j} T_i$. Using this notation, in (Ma et al., 2020a) Average Lagging was initially defined as follows:

$$AL = \frac{1}{\tau'(|\mathbf{X}|)} \sum_{i=1}^{\tau'(|\mathbf{X}|)} d_i - d_i^* \tag{1}$$

$$d_i^* = (i-1) \cdot \frac{\sum_{j=1}^{|\mathbf{X}|} T_j}{|\mathbf{Y}|} \tag{2}$$

where $\tau'(|\mathbf{X}|) = \min\{i | d_i = \sum_{j=1}^{|\mathbf{X}|} T_j\}$ is the index of the target token when the end of the source sentence is reached and d_i^* represents an oracle that, perfectly in sync with the speaker, starts to emit words as soon as the speech starts.

However, the authors noticed that this adaptation was not robust for models that tend to stop generating the hypothesis too early, that is systems that under-generate. This phenomenon is more likely to happen in SimulST than in SimulMT, for which AL was first proposed. For instance, the presence of long pauses in the speech may induce systems to generate the end of sentence token too early, even if the source utterance is not yet complete. As observed by the authors, when this phenomenon occurs, the lagging behind the oracle becomes negative. It follows that relatively good latency-quality trade-offs can be achieved thanks to inappropriate AL discounts in case of under-generation, while this does not reflect the reality. Thus, in (Ma et al., 2020a), Equation 1 was redefined as:

$$d_i^* = (i-1) \cdot \frac{\sum_{j=1}^{|\mathbf{X}|} T_j}{|\mathbf{Y}^*|} \tag{3}$$

assuming that the oracle delays d_i^* are computed based on the reference length rather than on the system hypothesis length.

3 The Problem of Over-Generation

In this paper, we point out a major issue of AL that arises in presence of over-generation. As we will see, AL improperly favors over-generating systems, potentially leading the community to wrong conclusions due to biased evaluations. To illustrate how over-generation affects AL computation, we consider a real example from the English→Spanish (en-es) section of MuST-C (Cattoni et al., 2021) tst-COMMON translated by the state-of-the-art Cross Attention Augmented Transducer (CAAT) system (Liu et al., 2021).

As shown in Figure 1, the prediction suffers from over-generation, especially in the first part of the sentence where more target words are produced compared to the reference. The system translates "*En primer lugar,*" instead of "*Primero,*", forcing all the predicted words to compare with the successive word in the reference. For instance, "*es*" in the CAAT output is computed against "*juego*" in the oracle and its very low lagging (49ms) is a considerable underestimation of the correct lagging with respect to the "*es*" word in the oracle (763ms). Likewise, "*de*" is assigned a negative lagging (−62ms) instead of the 652ms delay with respect to the time of "*de*" in the oracle. Finally, all the words generated before the end of the utterance (in our example 5000ms) and exceeding the reference length are compared with the last word of the oracle; the same happens to the first word emitted when the utterance is over, while the other words after the end of the utterance are ignored. As a result, the AL of CAAT output for this sentence is 198ms, an extremely low latency that does not reflect the truth. Indeed, if we correctly align and compare the words in the system output and the oracle, we see that lagging is on average 846ms.[3] This represents a problem, since the AL metric is rewarding an over-generating system, potentially hindering a fair comparison with other models.

In light of these observations, two questions arise. First, *what are the conditions leading to biased, i.e. underestimated, AL values?* The example above shows that the problem arises when: *i)* the system over-generates, and *ii)* the over-generated words appear before the utterance ends (the earlier

[3]The detailed calculation is presented in Appendix A.

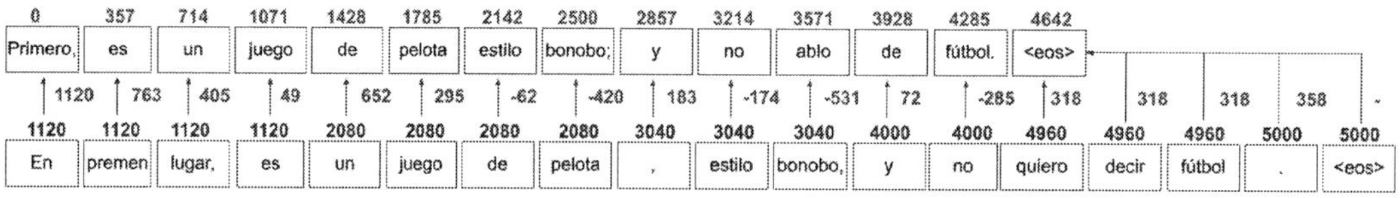

Figure 1: Example of AL computation between the oracle delays (in green) and the system delays (in blue). The lagging values (in red) are computed as the difference between the system and the oracle delays (the mapping is represented by an arrow). The 198ms AL is obtained by dividing the sum of the lagging (3379ms) by its count (17).

in time, the lower the final AL score will be). Second, *why was this problem overlooked when AL was introduced?* To answer this question, recall that AL for SimulST was initially proposed to evaluate systems showing a biased behaviour toward under-generation, with predictions length reaching at most the reference length. Indeed, earlier SimulST systems (Ma et al., 2020b) were designed to emit only one word at each time step. Consequently, even in the case of over-generation, it was extremely unlikely for the number of words emitted before the end of the utterance to be higher than the number of words in the reference. Moreover, additional words (if any) were generated only once the utterance was over. As mentioned above, the current AL implementation ignores all but the first word emitted at the end of the utterance. Therefore, the over-generation occurring at the end of the utterance does not affect the metric computation. Instead, AL is not robust to over-generation if it occurs before the end of the utterance, an extremely unlikely behavior in early systems but frequent in more recent ones, as we will see in the next section.

4 Over-generation frequency

To quantify the impact of over-generation on system evaluation, we check how frequently it occurs in the output of three SimulST systems: CAAT, the wait-k model by Ma et al. (2020b), and an offline model with the wait-k policy applied only at inference time (Papi et al., 2022; Gaido et al., 2022). We run three systems on the en-es section of MuST-C tst-COMMON by varying the k value at inference time in the range $\{3, 5, 7, 9, 11\}$. We measure over-generation in terms of average word length difference (AWLD) between systems predictions and the corresponding references, that is:

$$\text{AWLD} = \frac{1}{N}\sum_{s=1}^{N} |\mathbf{Y}| - |\mathbf{Y}^*| \quad (4)$$

where N is the number of samples in the corpus. Accordingly, positive AWLD values indicate that system predictions are on average longer than the reference (over-generation), while negative values indicate systems tendency to under-generate.

Model	k=3	k=5	k=7	k=9	k=11
wait-k	-5.57	-3.82	-2.30	-1.13	-0.74
offline wait-k	0.48	0.49	0.53	0.74	0.80
CAAT	1.57	0.96	0.61	0.35	0.18

Table 1: AWLD on MuST-C en-es tst-COMMON.

Table 1 shows that the wait-k system under-generates – as already noticed by Ma et al. (2020b) – while both CAAT and offline wait-k ones over-generate. In addition, while for the offline wait-k model the over-generation phenomenon is quite constant for each k value, for CAAT this diminishes as k increases. This indicates that over-generation is not an isolated phenomenon affecting only few sentences. On the contrary, it frequently occurs and automatic evaluation should take this into account.

5 Length Adaptive Average Lagging

Based on the observations made in Sections 3 and 4, we propose LAAL (Length-Adaptive Average Lagging), a modified version of AL accounting also for the over-generation phenomena. LAAL defines the oracle delays by dividing the utterance length by the maximum between the reference and the model prediction length. Specifically, we consider the reference length when the prediction is shorter (under-generation), and the prediction length when the prediction is longer (over-generation). This means that the correction is made at sentence level, making the metric applicable to a system disregarding its under- or over-generation tendency.

Figure 2 shows both the under-generation (in blue) and the over-generation (in green) cases. Analyzing the under-generation case, we can clearly see the motivation behind the correction made by Ma et al. (2020a): if we consider the prediction

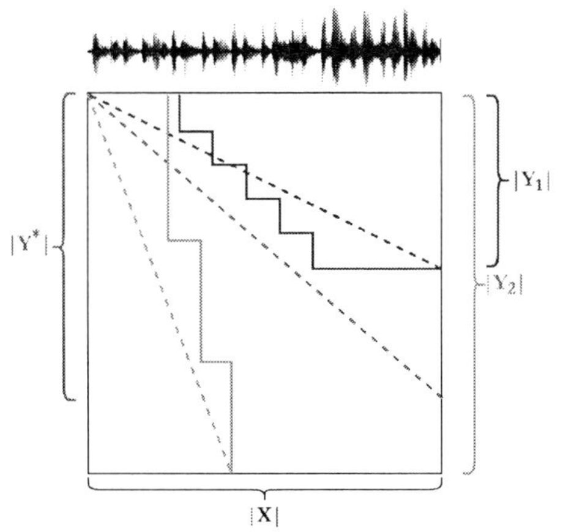

Figure 2: Example of under-generation (in blue), and over-generation (in green). The reference translation is represented by the red dashed line.

length ($|\mathbf{Y_1}|$) in the AL computation and the prediction is too short, the system is favoured since negative delays are summed (the blue straight line is mainly below the blue dashed line). A more reliable evaluation is obtained by considering the reference length ($|\mathbf{Y}^*|$), since the straight blue line is always above the dashed red line. By analyzing the over-generation case, we observe the opposite problem: if we consider the reference length ($|\mathbf{Y}^*|$) in the AL computation and the prediction is too long ($|\mathbf{Y_2}| > |\mathbf{Y}^*|$), the system is favoured since negative delays are summed (the straight green line stays almost always below the red dashed line). This can be corrected by considering the prediction length ($|\mathbf{Y_2}|$) instead. Therefore, to make a more reliable evaluation where neither under-generation nor over-generation are rewarded, we have to take the maximum between $|\mathbf{Y}^*|$ and $|\mathbf{Y}|$ in the delay computation (the two conditions are: $|\mathbf{Y}^*|$ if $|\mathbf{Y}| \leq |\mathbf{Y}^*|$, and $|\mathbf{Y}|$ if $|\mathbf{Y}| > |\mathbf{Y}^*|$). Accordingly, Equation 3 can be modified to obtain LAAL as:

$$d_i^* = (i-1) \cdot \frac{\sum_{j=1}^{|\mathbf{X}|} T_j}{\max\{|\mathbf{Y}|, |\mathbf{Y}^*|\}} \tag{5}$$

The difference between applying AL and LAAL to evaluate our three systems is shown in Table 2. As we can see, the LAAL of the wait-k system is almost equal to the AL, with differences from 17 to 73ms. Conversely, for the offline wait-k system we notice a quite constant increment in LAAL of about 120ms while for the CAAT system we observe that LAAL is visibly greater than AL, with differences from 117 to 283ms that are more marked at low latency. These differences are coherent with the over-generation trend observed in Table 1.

Model	Metric	k=3	k=5	k=7	k=9	k=11
wait-k	AL	1761	1970	2272	2582	2931
	LAAL	1778	2001	2332	2655	3003
offline wait-k	AL	1522	1959	2463	2926	3350
	LAAL	1682	2093	2588	3043	3457
CAAT	AL	735	1149	1533	1905	2265
	LAAL	1018	1365	1708	2046	2382

Table 2: AL and LAAL results in ms of the wait-k and CAAT systems on MuST-C en-es tst-COMMON.

Going back to the example in Figure 1, the latency value computed with LAAL is 707ms. Compared to the AL value of 198ms, this is much closer to the real measure of 846ms calculated in Section 3. In light of these observations, we can conclude that the LAAL metric gives a more reliable evaluation of the SimulST systems compared to AL.

6 Limitations

The proposed LAAL metric is a first step toward a more accurate evaluation of SimulST systems. Although in this work we focused on the over-generation problem, we did not address another limitation of AL (and, in turn, of LAAL). The problem is that, as shown in Section 2, AL compares the system output with an oracle that emits only one word at each time step, each one with a fixed word duration.[4] This means that, in its computation, we assume that the reference words are uniformly distributed in each utterance. However, considering that the amount of information contained in audio segments of the same length could be extremely different, this represents an unrealistic approximation. For instance, a speech segment can contain silences, long pauses, and the speech rate can vary considerably. As a consequence, the latency scores obtained can still largely differ from the latency experienced by the user. This advocates for the development of more human-centric solutions that go beyond AL-like metrics despite their success, accounting for different audio phenomena and their impact on the actual latency perceived by the users, also considering the visualization strategy selected (Karakanta et al., 2021; Papi et al., 2021). We leave this line of investigation for future work.

[4]In our example in Figure 1, the word duration is 357ms and is computed dividing the source audio duration (5000ms) by the reference length (14).

7 Conclusions

We showed through examples based on real systems that the current Average Lagging computation is inadequate to correctly measure SimulST performance in presence of over-generation phenomena. To overcome this problem, we proposed Length-Adaptive Average Lagging (LAAL), a latency metric that can effectively handle both under- and over-generation at sentence level, leading to a more reliable evaluation of SimulST systems.

Acknowledgments

This work has been carried out as part of the project Smarter Interpreting (`https://kunveno.digital/`) financed by CDTI Neotec funds.

References

Antonios Anastasopoulos, Ondřej Bojar, Jacob Bremerman, Roldano Cattoni, Maha Elbayad, Marcello Federico, Xutai Ma, Satoshi Nakamura, Matteo Negri, Jan Niehues, Juan Pino, Elizabeth Salesky, Sebastian Stüker, Katsuhito Sudoh, Marco Turchi, Alexander Waibel, Changhan Wang, and Matthew Wiesner. 2021. FINDINGS OF THE IWSLT 2021 EVALUATION CAMPAIGN. In *Proceedings of the 18th International Conference on Spoken Language Translation (IWSLT 2021)*, pages 1–29, Bangkok, Thailand (online). Association for Computational Linguistics.

Roldano Cattoni, Mattia Antonino Di Gangi, Luisa Bentivogli, Matteo Negri, and Marco Turchi. 2021. Must-c: A multilingual corpus for end-to-end speech translation. *Computer Speech & Language*, 66:101155.

Junkun Chen, Mingbo Ma, Renjie Zheng, and Liang Huang. 2021. Direct simultaneous speech-to-text translation assisted by synchronized streaming ASR. In *Findings of the Association for Computational Linguistics: ACL-IJCNLP 2021*, pages 4618–4624, Online. Association for Computational Linguistics.

Colin Cherry and George Foster. 2019. Thinking slow about latency evaluation for simultaneous machine translation.

Kyunghyun Cho and Masha Esipova. 2016. Can neural machine translation do simultaneous translation?

Maha Elbayad, Michael Ustaszewski, Emmanuelle Esperança-Rodier, Francis Brunet-Manquat, Jakob Verbeek, and Laurent Besacier. 2020. Online versus offline NMT quality: An in-depth analysis on English-German and German-English. In *Proceedings of the 28th International Conference on Computational Linguistics*, pages 5047–5058, Barcelona, Spain (Online). International Committee on Computational Linguistics.

Christian Fügen, Alex Waibel, and Muntsin Kolss. 2007. Simultaneous translation of lectures and speeches. *Machine Translation*, 21(4):209–252.

Marco Gaido, Sara Papi, Dennis Fucci, Giuseppe Fiameni, Matteo Negri, and Marco Turchi. 2022. Efficient yet competitive speech translation: FBK@IWSLT2022. In *Proceedings of the 19th International Conference on Spoken Language Translation (IWSLT 2022)*, pages 177–189, Dublin, Ireland (in-person and online). Association for Computational Linguistics.

Jiatao Gu, Graham Neubig, Kyunghyun Cho, and Victor O.K. Li. 2017. Learning to translate in real-time with neural machine translation. In *Proceedings of the 15th Conference of the European Chapter of the Association for Computational Linguistics: Volume 1, Long Papers*, pages 1053–1062, Valencia, Spain. Association for Computational Linguistics.

Navdeep Jaitly, Quoc V Le, Oriol Vinyals, Ilya Sutskever, David Sussillo, and Samy Bengio. 2016. An online sequence-to-sequence model using partial conditioning. In *Advances in Neural Information Processing Systems*, volume 29. Curran Associates, Inc.

Alina Karakanta, Sara Papi, Matteo Negri, and Marco Turchi. 2021. Simultaneous speech translation for live subtitling: from delay to display. In *Proceedings of the 1st Workshop on Automatic Spoken Language Translation in Real-World Settings (ASLTRW)*, pages 35–48.

Dan Liu, Mengge Du, Xiaoxi Li, Ya Li, and Enhong Chen. 2021. Cross attention augmented transducer networks for simultaneous translation. In *Proceedings of the 2021 Conference on Empirical Methods in Natural Language Processing*, pages 39–55, Online and Punta Cana, Dominican Republic. Association for Computational Linguistics.

Mingbo Ma, Liang Huang, Hao Xiong, Renjie Zheng, Kaibo Liu, Baigong Zheng, Chuanqiang Zhang, Zhongjun He, Hairong Liu, Xing Li, Hua Wu, and Haifeng Wang. 2019. STACL: Simultaneous translation with implicit anticipation and controllable latency using prefix-to-prefix framework. In *Proceedings of the 57th Annual Meeting of the Association for Computational Linguistics*, pages 3025–3036, Florence, Italy. Association for Computational Linguistics.

Xutai Ma, Mohammad Javad Dousti, Changhan Wang, Jiatao Gu, and Juan Pino. 2020a. SIMULEVAL: An evaluation toolkit for simultaneous translation. In *Proceedings of the 2020 Conference on Empirical Methods in Natural Language Processing: System Demonstrations*, pages 144–150, Online. Association for Computational Linguistics.

Xutai Ma, Juan Pino, and Philipp Koehn. 2020b. SimulMT to SimulST: Adapting simultaneous text translation to end-to-end simultaneous speech translation. In *Proceedings of the 1st Conference of the*

Asia-Pacific Chapter of the Association for Computational Linguistics and the 10th International Joint Conference on Natural Language Processing, pages 582–587, Suzhou, China. Association for Computational Linguistics.

Yusuke Oda, Graham Neubig, Sakriani Sakti, Tomoki Toda, and Satoshi Nakamura. 2014. Optimizing segmentation strategies for simultaneous speech translation. In *Proceedings of the 52nd Annual Meeting of the Association for Computational Linguistics (Volume 2: Short Papers)*, pages 551–556, Baltimore, Maryland. Association for Computational Linguistics.

Sara Papi, Marco Gaido, Matteo Negri, and Marco Turchi. 2022. Does simultaneous speech translation need simultaneous models? *arXiv preprint arXiv:2204.03783*.

Sara Papi, Matteo Negri, and Marco Turchi. 2021. Visualization: The missing factor in simultaneous speech translation. In *Proceedings of the Eighth Italian Conference on Computational Linguistics*.

Matt Post. 2018. A Call for Clarity in Reporting BLEU Scores. In *Proceedings of the Third Conference on Machine Translation: Research Papers*, pages 186–191, Belgium, Brussels. Association for Computational Linguistics.

Kanishka Rao, Haşim Sak, and Rohit Prabhavalkar. 2017. Exploring architectures, data and units for streaming end-to-end speech recognition with rnn-transducer. In *2017 IEEE Automatic Speech Recognition and Understanding Workshop (ASRU)*, pages 193–199. IEEE.

Xingshan Zeng, Liangyou Li, and Qun Liu. 2021. RealTranS: End-to-end simultaneous speech translation with convolutional weighted-shrinking transformer. In *Findings of the Association for Computational Linguistics: ACL-IJCNLP 2021*, pages 2461–2474, Online. Association for Computational Linguistics.

A Example Manual Latency Calculation

To manually compute the latency measure of the example shown in Figure 1, we compare the model output words to the reference words of the oracle by correctly aligning them. For instance "*En premen lugar,*" of the model prediction is aligned to "*Primero,*" of the oracle, "*es*" of the model prediction to "*es*" of the oracle, and so on. Therefore, the lagging calculation will be the following:

$$\begin{aligned}&(1120-0)+(1120-357)+(2080-714)+\\&(2080-1071)+(2080-1428)+(2080-1785)+\\&(3040-2142)+(3040-2500)+(4000-2857)+\\&(4000-3214)+(4960-3571)+(4960-4285)+\\&(5000-4642)=10994\end{aligned}$$

Then, we divide the lagging sum of 10994ms by their count (13) to obtain the latency of 846ms.

System Description on Automatic Simultaneous Translation Workshop

Zecheng Li[1*], Yue Sun[2], and Haoze Li[3]

[1]Zhejiang University, Hangzhou, China
[2]Xiamen University, Xiamen, China
[3]North China Institute of Aerospace Engineering, Langfang, China
[1]*lizechng@zju.edu.cn*
[2]*njauyuesun@qq.com*
[3]*lohanz@foxmail.com*

Abstract

This paper describes our system submitted on the third automatic simultaneous translation workshop at NAACL2022. We participate in the Chinese audio→English text direction of Chinese-to-English translation. Our speech-to-text system is a pipeline system, in which we resort to rhymological features for audio split, ASRT model for speech recoginition, STACL model for streaming text translation. To translate streaming text, we use wait-*k* policy *trained* to generate the target sentence concurrently with the source sentence, but always *k* words behind. We propose a competitive simultaneous translation system and rank 3rd in the audio input track. The code will release soon.

1 Introduction

Simultaneous translation refers to translating the message from the speaker to the audience in real-time without interrupting the speakers, which is a challenging task and has become an increasingly popular research field in recent years.

In this paper, we describe our system submitted at the 3rd automatic simultaneous translation workshop, which consists of a rhymeological features based audio split model, an end to end speech recognition model and a wait-*k*(Ma et al., 2019) based streaming text translation model. The system input is Chinese audio file and the output is English translation text. A temporary Streaming transcription is obtained by audio split and speech recognition model, then transmitted into machine translation model to get the target system output.

For automatic audio split model, we calculate the rhythmological features(Weninger et al., 2013) of the audio input, resort to adaptive policy to set short-term energy threshold and zero crossing rate threhold for speech split. For automatic speech recognition model, we use ASRT model[1], which is based DCNN model and CTC decoder(Graves et al., 2006). Whilst, we expand the training data set by adding Aishell-1(Bu et al., 2017) and Thchs-30(Wang and Zhang, 2015) datasets. For streaming text translation, our model is based on STACL(Ma et al., 2019). We use some human rules and the pre-trained language model to filter the parallel corpus. At the step of inference, we apply the wait-*k* words policy. Both the pre-processing and post-precessing are applied to improve the terminology translation and deal with the word error produced by the ASR system.

Since our submission is a pipeline system, the rest of this paper describes separately regards to audio split, automatic speech recognition and matchine translation sub-modules. We firstly describe the training and development datasets we used, then the data precessing methods is introduces. Secondly, we describe our system architecture and experiment results. Lastly, we draw a conclusion of our system by analyzing the experiments.

2 Dataset

For audio data of ASR, we use qianyan audio datasets provided by NAACL workshop(Zhang et al., 2021), Aishell-1(Bu et al., 2017), Thchs-30(Wang and Zhang, 2015). For text data of MT, we use CWMT19[2] and the simultaneous translation corpus provided by the organizer of the workshop.

2.1 Audio data

For qianyan audio datasets, we split each audio into sentences according to the sentence-level transcription. After processing, the blank part of all entire audio files was removed.

For other datasets, we firstly deal with transcription files by using rules to get path and filename of every transcription. Then using wave library to read audio files to get the duration time of each audio.

[1]https://github.com/nl8590687/ASRT_SpeechRecognition

[2]http://mteval.cipsc.org.cn:81/agreement/description

Proceedings of the Third Workshop on Automatic Simultaneous Translation, pages 18 - 21
July 15-16, 2022

Data Source	Duration	Size
Qianyan(NAACL)	65h	5.4G
Aishell-1	178h	14.51G
Thchs-30	40h	6.01G

Table 1: Zh-En audio training datasets.

In order to mitigate the matching issues between audio file and transcription text, we use pre-trained ASRT model to produce pronunciation results from audio input, and then obtain streaming text from pronumciation models. Table 1 shows the number of training data.

2.2 Text data

For CWMT19 and Baidu Speech Translation Corpus(BSTC)(Zhang et al., 2021) datasets, we firstly filter out the sentence whose English sentence is longer than 120 words. Meanwhile, there are a few Chinese characters in the data which are traditional characters. We convert them to simplified ones. Then all Chineses sentences are segmented with Jieba Chinese Segmentation Tool[3] and all English sentences are tokenized and truecased with Moses[4]. Lastly, Both Chinese and English data are encoded by BPE(Sennrich et al., 2015) with Subword-NMT[5] to train a bytes pairs encoding model.

3 System description

Our system consist of a rhymeological features based audio split model, an end to end speech recognition model, and a wait-*k* based streaming text translation model. The model training process for speech recognition and machine translation model are implemented on a device with four GPUs of Nvidia 1080ti.

3.1 Audio split

For automatic audio split model, we use the traditional acoustic methods. We firstly calculate the rhythmological features of the audio input based on Librosa audio processing library[6] and the openSMILE toolkit(Eyben et al., 2010). According to short-term energy and zero crossing rate of the rhythmological features, we can detect the endpoint of voice. This can detect all valid speech parts of a

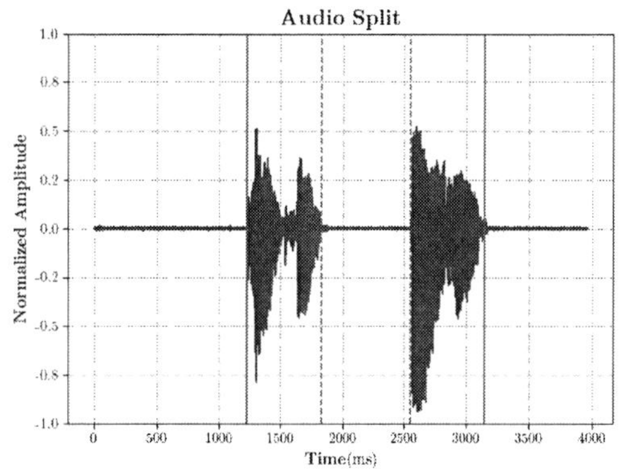

Figure 1: Audio Split Process. The solid red line is the reult of Step-1, and the dashed green line is the result of Step-2

Parameter	Step-1	Step-2
Frame length	400	240
Min. turbid interval	25	20
Short-term energy threhold	1.0	0.4
Zero crossing rate threhold	0.8	1.2

Table 2: Audio split model parameters.

section of speech. The endpoint detection consists of two steps. The first step is the overall endpoint detection used to segment the long audio file, the second step is the fine-tune of the splited audio. The audio split process is shown in Figure 1. The super-parameters we use are shown in the Table 2.

3.2 Speech recognition

The speech recognition model we use is ASRT model, based on deep convolutional neural network and long-short memory neural network, attention mechanism and CTC to implement.

We firstly limit the maximum length of splited audio to 16 seconds, as the input of ASRT model. The speech recognition model will output the corresponding pronunciation sequence. Then we resort to probability map based maximum entropy Markov model to convert the pronunciation sequence to recogized text. To improve the recognition accuracy, we use the model pre-trained on AiShell-1 and Thchs-30 datasets and fine-tune on audio dataset provided by NAACL workshop. We list the model configuration in Table 3

3.3 Machine translation

We use STACL as our machine translation model. We train the model for over two days,

[3]https://github.com/fxsjy/jieba
[4]https://github.com/moses-smt/mosesdecoder
[5]https://github.com/rsennrich/subword-nmt
[6]https://github.com/librosa/librosa

Configuration	Value
Audio length	1600
Feature length	200
Label length	64
Channels	1
Output size	1428
Optimizer	Adam

Table 3: Speech recognition model configuration

Configuration	Value
Encoder/Decoder depth	6
Attention heads	8
Word Embedding	512
Chinese Vacabulary size	10000
English Vacabulary size	10000
Optimizer	Adam

Table 4: Machine translation model configuration

the BLEU(Papineni et al., 2002) score increased rapidly at the beginning and the growth slowed after 20 hours. After the loss converged, we save the last checkpoint as the final model. We list the model configuration in Table 4 and training parameters in Table 5.

The simultaneous policy we use is wait-k, which first wait k source words, and then translates concurrently with the reset of source sentence, i.e., the output is always k words behind the input.

We implement fine-tuning on the STACL model using the BSTC dataset to improve the translation quality on simultaneous translation task. Since fine-tuning is effective to build a domain-adaptive model.

4 Experiment

In this section, we evaluate our system on the development set of the Baidu Speech Translation Corpus. The two used metrics are case-sensitive detokenized BLEU(Papineni et al., 2002) and Consecutive Wait(CW)(Gu et al., 2016), for translation quality and latency respectively. CW considers on how many source words are waited for consecutively between two target words, and thus larget CW means longer latency.

Parameter	Value
Label smoothing	0.1
Learning rate	2.0
Warmup steps	8000
Maximum sentence length	120

Table 5: Machine translation model training parameters

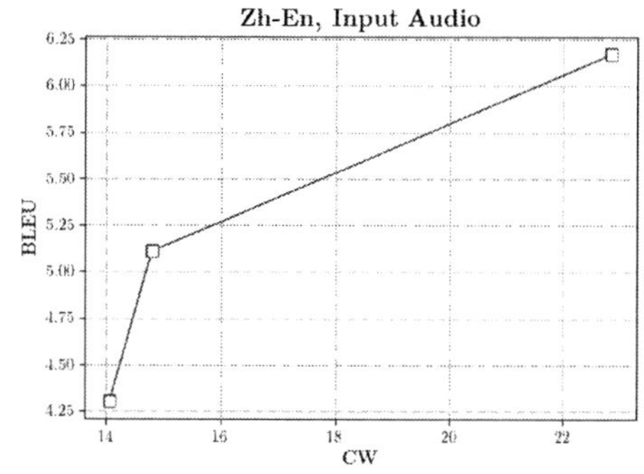

Figure 2: Experimental Result of speech-to-text track

We set the threshold k in the wait-k policy to various values and get multiple results, as shown in Figure 2. Due to the speech in the development set is difficult for ASR model trained ourselves, resulting in a high character error rate. The errors caused by ASR are brought to MT, and thus the BLEU is much lower than that in the text-to-text track.

5 Conclusion

This paper describe our submission to the 3rd automatic simultaneous workshop at NAACL2022. We detail our process of data filtering and model training. The Consecutive Wait(CW) of the best point reached to 14.06, while we get the BLEU value of 6.17 in the audio input track. In future work, we will continue to research on end-to-end speech translation model.

References

Hui Bu, Jiayu Du, Xingyu Na, Bengu Wu, and Hao Zheng. 2017. Aishell-1: An open-source mandarin speech corpus and a speech recognition baseline. In *2017 20th Conference of the Oriental Chapter of the International Coordinating Committee on Speech Databases and Speech I/O Systems and Assessment (O-COCOSDA)*, pages 1–5. IEEE.

Florian Eyben, Martin Wöllmer, and Björn Schuller. 2010. Opensmile: the munich versatile and fast open-source audio feature extractor. In *Proceedings of the 18th ACM international conference on Multimedia*, pages 1459–1462.

Alex Graves, Santiago Fernández, Faustino Gomez, and Jürgen Schmidhuber. 2006. Connectionist temporal classification: labelling unsegmented sequence data with recurrent neural networks. In *Proceedings of the 23rd international conference on Machine learning*, pages 369–376.

Jiatao Gu, Graham Neubig, Kyunghyun Cho, and Victor OK Li. 2016. Learning to translate in real-time with neural machine translation. *arXiv preprint arXiv:1610.00388*.

Mingbo Ma, Liang Huang, Hao Xiong, Renjie Zheng, Kaibo Liu, Baigong Zheng, Chuanqiang Zhang, Zhongjun He, Hairong Liu, Xing Li, Hua Wu, and Haifeng Wang. 2019. STACL: Simultaneous translation with implicit anticipation and controllable latency using prefix-to-prefix framework. In *Proceedings of the 57th Annual Meeting of the Association for Computational Linguistics*, pages 3025–3036, Florence, Italy. Association for Computational Linguistics.

Kishore Papineni, Salim Roukos, Todd Ward, and Wei-Jing Zhu. 2002. Bleu: a method for automatic evaluation of machine translation. In *Proceedings of the 40th annual meeting of the Association for Computational Linguistics*, pages 311–318.

Rico Sennrich, Barry Haddow, and Alexandra Birch. 2015. Neural machine translation of rare words with subword units. *arXiv preprint arXiv:1508.07909*.

Dong Wang and Xuewei Zhang. 2015. Thchs-30: A free chinese speech corpus. *arXiv preprint arXiv:1512.01882*.

Felix Weninger, Florian Eyben, Björn W Schuller, Marcello Mortillaro, and Klaus R Scherer. 2013. On the acoustics of emotion in audio: what speech, music, and sound have in common. *Frontiers in psychology*, 4:292.

Ruiqing Zhang, Xiyang Wang, Chuanqiang Zhang, Zhongjun He, Hua Wu, Zhi Li, Haifeng Wang, Ying Chen, and Qinfei Li. 2021. Bstc: A large-scale chinese-english speech translation dataset. *arXiv preprint arXiv:2104.03575*.

System Description on Third Automatic Simultaneous Translation Workshop

Zhang Yiqiao
College of science, Huazhong Agricultural University, Wuhan 430070, China
qiaoyizhang@webmail.hzau.edu.cn

Abstract

This paper shows my submission to the Third Automatic Simultaneous Translation Workshop at NAACL2022. The submission includes Chinese audio to English text task, Chinese text to English text tast, and English text to Spanish text task. For the two text-to-text tasks, I use the STACL model of PaddleNLP. As for the audio-to-text task, I first use DeepSpeech2 to translate the audio into text, then apply the STACL model to handle the text-to-text task. The submission results show that the used method can get low delay with a few training samples.

1 Introduction

The submitted system consists of two parts. One is audio to text system, which can translate Chinese audio into English text. The second part is the text-to-text model, which can translate source text into the target language.

In the text-to-text translation task, the used system is STACL model (Ma et al., 2019). All training data are processed by Byte Pair Encoding (Sennrich et al., 2016). In addition, the strategies used by the model in training and inference are the same. For example, if the wait-k strategy in inference is 1, the wait-k in training is also 1.

In the audio to text translation task, the DeepSpeech2 model (Amodei et al., 2015) is used as the preprocessing of the STACL model. The DeepSpeech2 model can translate audio (Chinese) segments into text (Chinese) segments and then input the segments into the STACL model to generate the target-language text.

The submitted results show that the used STACL model has a low delay for text translation tasks. But the system can only generate the results with a high delay in the audio translation task.

The rest of the paper is organized as follows. Section 2 describes the training data used in the submitted system. Section 3 describes the model, training strategy, and results. The conclusions are given in Section 4.

2 Datasets

In this section, I describe the Datasets.

2.1 Zh-En Text Translation Dataset

The dataset used for the Chinese-to-English(Zh-En) translation task is extracted from AST, which is provided by the NAACL workshop. This data set contains 214 JSON files, and each JSON file contains parallel Chinese vs. English corpus. The data, which is extracted from these JSON files, contains 37,901 Chinese vs. English samples. After byte pair encoding, the samples are used to train the Zh-En translation model.

The BPE vocabulary of the Zh-En translation task can be found in the Github project of PaddleNLP (Contributors, 2021).

2.2 En-Es Text Translation Dataset

The dataset used for the English-to-Spanish(En-Es) text translation task was obtained from the United Nations Parallel Corpus(Ziemski et al., 2016). The En-Es dataset contains 21,911,121 samples. After byte pair encoding, the dataset is used to train the En-Es text translation model.

For obtaining the BPE vocabulary, I segment the source dataset into subword units by Subword Neural Machine Translation (Sennrich et al., 2015). The code for segmentation can be found in (Sennrich, 2021).

2.3 Audio-to-Test Dataset

The training data of the Chinese speech recognition model is AISHELL (Bu et al., 2017), which is an open-source Mandarin speech corpus. In the submitted system, I only use the pre-trained model of the DeepSpeech2 model on AISHELL.

Proceedings of the Third Workshop on Automatic Simultaneous Translation, pages 22 - 24
July 15-16, 2022 ©2022 Association for Computational Linguistics

Parameter	Value
wait-k	1 or 3
max epoch	30
batch size	512
learning rate	2.0
max length	256
n layer	6

Table 1: Training parameters in Zh-En translation model

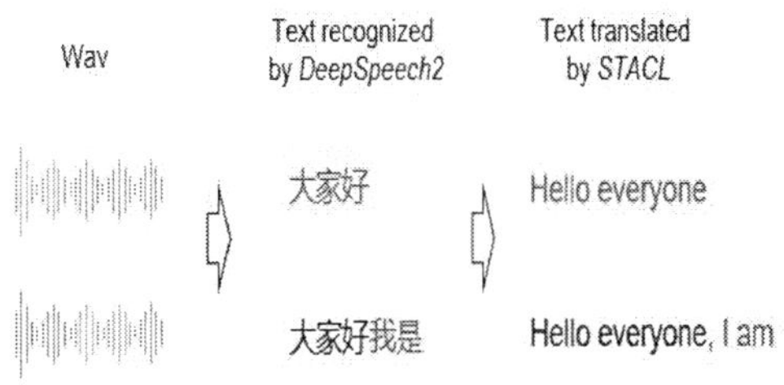

Figure 1: Frame for audio translation system

3 Models and Results

This section shows the models used in the submitted system and discusses the results.

3.1 Text Translation System

3.1.1 STACL model

In the text translation task, the model is STACL (Ma et al., 2019), which is a translation architecture for all simultaneous interpreting scenarios. For train the model, the wait-k strategy is adopted. The model will wait for k words of the source text and then start to translate. For example, when k is 2, the model only starts translating the first word of the target language after obtaining the second word of the source text.

In the inference process, the model decodes one word at a time. When the sentences to be translated are all read, the untranslated sentences will be completed at once.

3.1.2 Results in Zh-En task

In the Zh-En translation task, I trained the model with wait-k = 1 and wait-k = 3. The details of training parameters are shown in table 1.

When the wait-k is 1, the AL of the submitted result is -1.28, and the BLEU is 14.86. When the wait-k is 3, the AL is -0.52, and the BLUE is 14.84. The two results have almost the same accuracy, demonstrating that the used dataset may not be sufficient for the translation task.

3.1.3 Results in En-Es task

In the En-Es translation task, the max epoch is set as 1, and other parameters are the same as table 1.

The AL of the submitted result is -1.61, and the BLEU is 11.82.

3.2 Audio Translation System

3.2.1 DeepSpeech2 model

Deepspeech2 is an end-to-end automatic speech recognition system based on the PaddlePaddle deep learning framework (Amodei et al., 2015). In order to translate the speech data into the corresponding target-language text, I first segment the audio, use deepspeech2 to covert the voice segment into text, and then translate the recognized text into the target language through the STACL model. Figure 1 shows the workflow of speech recognition translation.

3.2.2 Results

Since each segment contains multiple Chinese characters, decoding only one character at a time will lead to excessive delay (CW value). To overcome this issue, I decoded two characters at once. The CW of submitted results is 19.21, and the BLEU is 7.3.

4 Conclusion

This paper describes my submitted system at the Third Automatic Simultaneous Translation Workshop. The system submitted has a low delay. I will conduct a further study about the speech recognition strategy in the future.

Acknowledgements

This document has been adapted by Steven Bethard, Ryan Cotterell and Rui Yan from the instructions for earlier ACL and NAACL proceedings, including those for ACL 2019 by Douwe Kiela and Ivan Vulić, NAACL 2019 by Stephanie Lukin and Alla Roskovskaya, ACL 2018 by Shay Cohen, Kevin Gimpel, and Wei Lu, NAACL 2018 by Margaret Mitchell and Stephanie Lukin, BibTEX suggestions for (NA)ACL 2017/2018 from Jason Eisner, ACL 2017 by Dan Gildea and Min-Yen Kan, NAACL 2017 by Margaret Mitchell, ACL 2012 by Maggie Li and Michael White, ACL 2010 by Jing-Shin Chang and Philipp Koehn, ACL 2008 by Johanna D. Moore, Simone Teufel, James Allan, and Sadaoki Furui, ACL 2005 by Hwee Tou Ng and

Kemal Oflazer, ACL 2002 by Eugene Charniak and Dekang Lin, and earlier ACL and EACL formats written by several people, including John Chen, Henry S. Thompson and Donald Walker. Additional elements were taken from the formatting instructions of the *International Joint Conference on Artificial Intelligence* and the *Conference on Computer Vision and Pattern Recognition*.

References

Dario Amodei, Rishita Anubhai, Eric Battenberg, Carl Case, Jared Casper, Bryan Catanzaro, Jingdong Chen, Mike Chrzanowski, Adam Coates, Greg Diamos, Erich Elsen, Jesse H. Engel, Linxi Fan, Christopher Fougner, Tony Han, Awni Y. Hannun, Billy Jun, Patrick LeGresley, Libby Lin, Sharan Narang, Andrew Y. Ng, Sherjil Ozair, Ryan Prenger, Jonathan Raiman, Sanjeev Satheesh, David Seetapun, Shubho Sengupta, Yi Wang, Zhiqian Wang, Chong Wang, Bo Xiao, Dani Yogatama, Jun Zhan, and Zhenyao Zhu. 2015. Deep speech 2: End-to-end speech recognition in english and mandarin. *CoRR*, abs/1512.02595.

Hui Bu, Jiayu Du, Xingyu Na, Bengu Wu, and Hao Zheng. 2017. AISHELL-1: an open-source mandarin speech corpus and A speech recognition baseline. *CoRR*, abs/1709.05522.

PaddleNLP Contributors. 2021. Paddlenlp: An easy-to-use and high performance nlp library. `https://github.com/PaddlePaddle/PaddleNLP`.

Mingbo Ma, Liang Huang, Hao Xiong, Renjie Zheng, Kaibo Liu, Baigong Zheng, Chuanqiang Zhang, Zhongjun He, Hairong Liu, Xing Li, Hua Wu, and Haifeng Wang. 2019. STACL: Simultaneous translation with implicit anticipation and controllable latency using prefix-to-prefix framework. In *Proceedings of the 57th Annual Meeting of the Association for Computational Linguistics*, pages 3025–3036, Florence, Italy. Association for Computational Linguistics.

Rico Sennrich. 2021. Subword neural machine translation. `https://github.com/rsennrich/subword-nmt`.

Rico Sennrich, Barry Haddow, and Alexandra Birch. 2015. Neural machine translation of rare words with subword units. *CoRR*, abs/1508.07909.

Rico Sennrich, Barry Haddow, and Alexandra Birch. 2016. Neural machine translation of rare words with subword units. In *Proceedings of the 54th Annual Meeting of the Association for Computational Linguistics (Volume 1: Long Papers)*, pages 1715–1725, Berlin, Germany. Association for Computational Linguistics.

Michał Ziemski, Marcin Junczys-Dowmunt, and Bruno Pouliquen. 2016. The united nations parallel corpus v1.0.

End-to-End Simultaneous Speech Translation with Pretraining and Distillation: Huawei Noah's System for AutoSimTranS 2022

Xingshan Zeng, Pengfei Li, Liangyou Li, Qun Liu
Huawei Noah's Ark Lab
{zeng.xingshan,lipengfei111,liliangyou,qun.liu}@huawei.com

Abstract

This paper describes the system submitted to AutoSimTrans 2022 from Huawei Noah's Ark Lab, which won the first place in the audio input track of the Chinese-English translation task. Our system is based on RealTranS, an end-to-end simultaneous speech translation model. We enhance the model with pretraining, by initializing the acoustic encoder with ASR encoder, and the semantic encoder and decoder with NMT encoder and decoder, respectively. To relieve the data scarcity, we further construct pseudo training corpus as a kind of knowledge distillation with ASR data and the pretrained NMT model. Meanwhile, we also apply several techniques to improve the robustness and domain generalizability, including punctuation removal, token-level knowledge distillation and multi-domain finetuning. Experiments show that our system significantly outperforms the baselines at all latency and also verify the effectiveness of our proposed methods.

1 Introduction

Simultaneous Speech Translation (ST) task (Fügen et al., 2007; Oda et al., 2014) aims to translate speech into the corresponding text in another language while reading the source speech. Prior works mainly focus on the cascaded solution, i.e., first recognize the speech with a streaming ASR model and then translate into the target language with simultaneous NMT (Ma et al., 2019) model. Such cascaded systems can leverage off-the-shelf ASR and NMT systems, which have large-scale data for training.

Recently, end-to-end simultaneous ST models are also proposed (Ren et al., 2020; Zeng et al., 2021) and have shown promising improvements towards cascaded models when experimented on the same amount of data, especially in low latency requirement. End-to-end models are believed to have the advantages of lower latency, smaller model size and less error propagation (Weiss et al., 2017), but suffer from data scarcity. A well-trained end-to-end model typically needs a large amount of training data. To alleviate the data scarcity problem, pretraining (Xu et al., 2021; Li et al., 2021) and data augmentation (Bahar et al., 2019; Jia et al., 2019) are two main techniques. We examine the effectiveness of the two techniques for improving end-to-end models in this work.

Specifically, our end-to-end ST model follows RealTranS (Zeng et al., 2021), an encoder-decoder model and the encoder is decoupled into acoustic encoder and semantic encoder. The acoustic encoder is used to extract acoustic features which has a similar function as the ASR encoder. Therefore we initialize it with a pretrained ASR encoder. The semantic encoder is required to learn semantic knowledge, which benefits the translation task, so we initialize it with a pretrained NMT encoder. The decoder is also initialized with a pretrained NMT decoder to produce target text decoding. For data augmentation, we construct pseudo ST corpus based on ASR data and the pretrained NMT model. The ground-truth transcription is translated into target language texts, and so speech-transcription-translation triplets for ST training are built. This is also known as sequence-level knowledge distillation (Kim and Rush, 2016). Generally, the NMT data can also be augmented with a TTS model to generate pseudo speech. However, the data quality highly depends on the TTS performance and it is hard for TTS to produce voices similar to those in real scenarios. Thus we do not utilize this method and leave it to the future work. Another popular technique for audio data augmentation is SpecAugment (Park et al., 2019; Bahar et al., 2019), which randomly masks a block of consecutive time steps and/or mel frequency channels of the input speech features during training. It is a simple and low-implementation cost method and has been shown effective in avoiding overfitting and improving ro-

Proceedings of the Third Workshop on Automatic Simultaneous Translation, pages 25 - 33
July 15-16, 2022

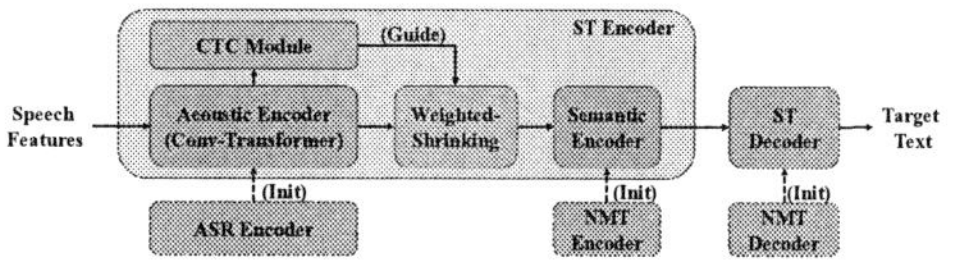

Figure 1: Our RealTranS model with pretraining.

bustness. We apply it to all audio-related model training.

The training procedure for our ST model mainly contains three steps: ASR and NMT pretraining, large-scale training on the constructed pseudo data, and finetuning on the in-domain data. During training, we remove all the punctuation in source text in audio-related training (i.e., excluding NMT pretraining) to relieve the learning burden and improve recognition quality. To enhance the final performance after finetuning, we also utilize token-level knowledge distillation from the full-sentence NMT model and multi-domain finetuning trick.

Our model is used to participate in the audio input track of the AutoSimTrans 2022 Chinese-English translation task. In this track, an in-domain ST data called BSTC (Zhang et al., 2021) (contains about 70 hours of audios) is provided, which is very limited. Therefore, assisted with extra ASR and NMT data, we use the aforementioned techniques to achieve remarkable improvement at all latency requirement, which results in winning the first place of the track. We also conduct more experiments to examine the effectiveness of our used techniques. The experiments show that all of our used methods contribute to the improvement of the final model.

2 Model Description

We build our model based on RealTranS (Zeng et al., 2021), an end-to-end simultaneous speech translation model with its encoder decoupled into acoustic encoder and semantic encoder (see Figure 1). With a CTC module guiding the acoustic encoder to produce acoustic-level features, the decoupling relieves the burden of the ST encoder and makes the two separate modules focus on different knowledge, which benefits the model training.

RealTranS leverages the unidirectional Conv-Transformer (Huang et al., 2020) as the acoustic encoder for gradual downsampling, and weighted-shrinking for bridging the modality gap between speech and text. With weighted-shrinking, long speech features are shrunk to similar lengths as their corresponding transcription, which makes the input of the semantic encoder more similar to the input of NMT encoder. In this way, the difficulty of knowledge transferring when we initialize the semantic encoder with NMT encoder becomes smaller. Apart from the semantic encoder, we also initialize the acoustic encoder with pretrained ASR encoder, and the decoder with pretrained NMT decoder, which has been shown very useful in boosting the performance (Xu et al., 2021).

For simultaneous policy, we use the wait-k-stride-n policy (Zeng et al., 2021), which has shown promising improvement over the conventional wait-k policy (Ma et al., 2019).

3 Training Procedure

Our model training consists of three steps: ASR and NMT pretraining, large-scale training on the constructed pseudo data, and finetuning on the in-domain data. Each step may contain different techniques to enhance model performance and we will describe them in-detailed as follows.

3.1 Pretraining

We first describe how we pretrain our ASR and NMT models.

ASR Pretraining. Our ASR model follows the architecture of Conv-Transformer Transducer proposed by Huang et al. (2020). A Transducer model contains an audio encoder, a prediction net and a joint net, where the audio encoder is used for initializing the acoustic encoder of our ST model and the rest discarded. For each frame in input speech features, the model first predicts either a token label from the vocabulary or a special blank symbol. When a label is predicted, the model continues to predict the next output; when the model predicts a blank symbol, it proceeds to the next frame indicating no more labels can be predicted with current frames. Therefore, for each input speech $\boldsymbol{x}$, the model will give $T_x + T_z$ predictions, where T_x (the length of $\boldsymbol{x}$) is the number of blank symbols and T_z is the number of token labels representing the output transcription $\boldsymbol{z}$. A Transducer model computes the following marginalized distribution and maximizes it during training:

$$p(\boldsymbol{z}|\boldsymbol{x}) = \sum_{\hat{\boldsymbol{z}} \in \mathcal{A}(\boldsymbol{x},\boldsymbol{z})} \prod_{i=1}^{T_x+T_z} p(\hat{z}_i|x_1, ..., x_{t_i}, z_0, ..., z_{u_{i-1}}) \quad (1)$$

where $\mathcal{A}(\boldsymbol{x}, \boldsymbol{z})$ is the set containing all valid alignment paths such that removing the blank symbols in $\hat{z}$ yields z. The summation of probabilities of all alignment paths is computed efficiently with forward-backward algorithm.

As there is no ASR data provided, we collect large-scale ASR datasets from both publicly available websites and our internal system (the statistics of the datasets are in Table 1) for training. During training, we also add additive Gaussian noise and apply speed perturbation (Ko et al., 2015) and SpecAugment (Park et al., 2019) for data augmentation and model robustness.

Finally, our pretrained ASR model gets the performance of 11.35% WER (Word Error Rate) in BSTC development set.

NMT Pretraining. We pretrain our NMT model with CeMAT (Li et al., 2022), a sequence-to-sequence pretraining model but with a bidirectional decoder, which has been shown to be effective in NMT tasks. CeMAT can be pretrained on large-scale bilingual and monolingual corpus. As no additional text data are available, we only use the dynamic dual-masking algorithm to improve performance. Given an input source sentence z, we first sample a masking ratio μ from a uniform distribution between $[0.1, 0.2]$, then randomly mask a subset of source words according to μ. For the corresponding target sentence y, we also use a uniform distribution between $[0.2, 0.5]$ to sample a masking ratio υ. Following CeMAT, we set $\upsilon \geq \mu$ to force the bidirectional decoder to obtain more information from the encoder. For monolingual, we create pseudo bilignual text by copying the sentence, then sample $\upsilon = \mu$ from a uniform distribution between $[0.3, 0.4]$ and mask the same subset on both sides. After dual-masking, we get the new sentence pair $(\hat{z}, \hat{y})$, which will be used for jointly training the encoder and decoder by predicting masked tokens on both sides. The final training objective is formulated as follows:

$$\begin{aligned}\mathcal{L} = - \sum_{(\hat{z},\hat{y})} \lambda \sum_{y_j \in y^{mask}} \log P(y_j|\hat{z}, \hat{y}) \\ +(1-\lambda) \sum_{z_i \in z^{mask}} \log P(z_i|\hat{z})\end{aligned} \tag{2}$$

where y^{mask} are the set of masked target words, z^{mask} are the set of masked source words, and λ is a hyper-parameter to balance the influence of both sides. Following CeMAT, we set $\lambda = 0.7$.

Our NMT pretraining procedure can be summarized as three sub-steps. We first train a basic NMT model using the provided general-domain bilingual data (see Table 1), and generate pseudo target sentences based on the source text from the ASR data used in ASR pretraining. To improve the quality of the pseudo corpus, we use HintedBT (Ramnath et al., 2021) to score each generated sentences. Next, we combine the bilingual data, the pseudo corpus and the monolingual text (from the used ASR data) to pretrain CeMAT. Finally, we finetune it on the bilingual and pseudo corpus including the in-domain data (i.e. text part in BSTC dataset) to produce our final NMT model.

The encoder and decoder of the NMT model is used to initialize the semantic encoder and decoder of our ST model, respectively. It is also used to generate pseudo ST data in next subsection.

Our NMT model achieves BLEU score of 21.82 in BSTC development set, and also won the second place in the streaming transcription input track of the Chinese-English translation task.

3.2 Training on Pseudo Data (Distillation)

As the provided ST data is limited (about 70 hours annotated data), it is difficult to directly train an end-to-end model only with the provided data. We decide to construct pseudo data from our used ASR data – we translate the Chinese transcription into English translation with our pretrained NMT model so that we get a large-scale pseudo ST corpus with audio-transcription-translation triplets. In this way, we can leverage large-scale unannotated audios and distill knowledge from the NMT model. We remove all the punctuation in transcription (as the ASR data comes from different domains, some of them contain punctuation but some not) to make it consistent during training.

We first train our model (initialized with the pretrained modules described in Section 3.1) on the pseudo data with multi-path wait-k training (Elbayad et al., 2020) to cover all possible k values. Specifically, k value will be uniformly sampled from $K = [1, ..., |K|]$ for each training sample during training while we keep the n value in wait-k-stride-n policy at 2. In this way, the model can learn knowledge for different latency requirements. The training objectives follows RealTranS and contain the CTC loss ($\mathcal{L}_{CTC}$) (Graves et al., 2006) with a blank penalty ($\mathcal{L}_{BP}$) (Zeng et al., 2021). We omit their equations here and refer the readers to Zeng et al. (2021) for details. The translation loss are defined as follows:

$$\mathcal{L}_{ST} = -\sum_{(\boldsymbol{x},\boldsymbol{y})\in\mathcal{D},k\sim\mathcal{U}(K)} \prod_{t=1}^{T_y} p(y_t|y_{<t}, x'_{\leq g_{k,n}(t)}) \quad (3)$$

where $\boldsymbol{x}$ and $\boldsymbol{y}$ are the input speech features and the output token sequence, and $\mathcal{D}$ is the training corpus. $y_{<t}$ denotes the target tokens before time step t and $x'_{\leq g_{k,n}(t)}$ represents the first $g_{k,n}(t)$ source features after weighted-shrinking (generally, one shrunk feature may represent one source token as they are shrunk based on CTC output probability) with $g_{k,n}(t) = n\lfloor(t-1)/n\rfloor + k$. Finally, the total training objective is:

$$\mathcal{L}_{PT} = \mathcal{L}_{ST} + \alpha\mathcal{L}_{CTC} + \beta\mathcal{L}_{BP} \quad (4)$$

where α and β are the hyper-parameters to balance the losses, which are set to $\alpha = 1.0$ and $\beta = 0.5$. During training, we also apply SpecAugment.

3.3 Finetuning on In-Domain Data

After the large-scale training on pseudo data, we use the in-domain data (i.e., the provided 70 hours BSTC data) for finetuning. To be consistent with the training in the previous step, we also remove all punctuation in the source texts for CTC loss. During finetuning, there are mainly two aspects that are different from the large-scale training in the previous step. First, we fix the k value rather than use the multi-path wait-k training and train several models with different k as the in-domain data is very small. Second, we add a token-level knowledge distillation (KD) loss guided by the full-sentence NMT model pretrained in Section 3.1. Note that the input for the NMT model are the source texts with punctuation preserved. In this way, the final ST model can also learn from text translation. The KD loss is defined as follows:

$$\begin{aligned}\mathcal{L}_{KD} = -\sum_{(\boldsymbol{x},\boldsymbol{z},\boldsymbol{y})\in\mathcal{D}_{ST}} \sum_{t=1}^{T_y}\sum_{k=1}^{|V|} q(y_t = v_k|y_{<t}, \boldsymbol{z}) \\ \times \log p(y_t = v_k|y_{<t}, x'_{\leq g_{k,n}(t)})\end{aligned} \quad (5)$$

where $\boldsymbol{x}$, $\boldsymbol{z}$ and $\boldsymbol{y}$ are the input speech features, the input source texts and the output token sequence, and $\mathcal{D}_{ST}$ is the in-domain training corpus. Therefore, the total finetuning objective is:

$$\mathcal{L}_{FT} = (1-\gamma)\mathcal{L}_{ST} + \gamma\mathcal{L}_{KD} + \alpha\mathcal{L}_{CTC} + \beta\mathcal{L}_{BP} \quad (6)$$

where γ controls the tradeoff between the ST and KD losses and is set to 0.2. We set $\alpha = 1.0$ and $\beta = 0.5$.

Dataset	SRC Speech	SRC Text	TGT Text	#Hours	#Sents
CWMT21	×	✓	✓	–	9M
Internal	✓	✓	Pseudo	10K	11M
WenetSpeech	✓	✓	Pseudo	10K	14M
BSTC	✓	✓	✓	70	38K

Table 1: The statistics of the used datasets.

Note that in our experiments, we utilize multi-domain finetuning rather than finetuning only with the in-domain data, i.e., we also randomly sample similar number of training samples from the constructed pseudo data for finetuning. This improves domain generalizabiliy of our model. More analysis can be found in Section 4.3.

4 Experiments

4.1 Experimental Setup

Datasets. We introduce the details of the datasets we use here. Table 1 displays the statistics of them. CWMT21[1] is the NMT data in general domain provided by the organizer. We mainly use it to pretrain our NMT model. Internal and WenetSpeech are large-scale ASR datasets, both of which contain about 10K hours of audios. WenetSpeech is mainly collected from YouTube and Podcast and is publicly available[2], while Internal comes from our internal system, containing conversations or readings from multiple domains. The transcription in them are translated into target texts with our pretrained NMT model, which results in large-scale pseudo ST data. Finally, BSTC is the in-domain ST data provided by the organizer. It is used to finetune our NMT model (with source texts and target texts) and the final ST model.

The punctuation in source texts is processed with different ways according to different training procedure (see Section 3 for details), while that in target texts is always preserved. We also filter the data based on the lengths of source and target texts. We follow Zhang and Feng (2021) and use char-level tokenization on the Chinese sentences, while we apply sentencepiece[3] (Kudo and Richardson, 2018) to generate subword vocabulary for English.

System Setting. We use 128-dimensional log-mel filterbank as acoustic features, calculated with 20 ms window and 10 ms stride and normalized by

[1] http://mteval.cipsc.org.cn:81/agreement/AutoSimTrans

[2] https://wenet.org.cn/WenetSpeech/

[3] https://github.com/google/sentencepiece

Global CMVN (cepstral mean and variance normalization). Our acoustic encoder contains two blocks of Conv-Transformer (Huang et al., 2020). In the first block, we have two 2-D convolution layers with stride 2 and four layers of transformer encoder; while in the second block, we have three 1-D convolution layers with one of them is stride 2 (others 1) and 16 layers of transformer encoder. This results in total $8\times$ downsampling and introduces a 100ms look-ahead window. In the first block, transformer layers are with 384 dimension and 6 attention heads, while in the second block they are with 512 dimension and 8 attention heads. For the semantic encoder and decoder, as they are initialized with the NMT model, they follow the deep encoder, shallow decoder architecture to improve inference efficiency, with 12 encoder layers, 3 decoder layers, 12 attention heads and 768 hidden size.

Our model is trained with 24 NVIDIA Tesla V100 GPUs, each with a max-tokens of 2048 (i.e., maximum of 2048 text tokens in one batch). We use Adam optimizer (Kingma and Ba, 2015) during model training with $2e^{-3}$ learning rate and 10000 warm-up steps, followed by the inverse square root scheduler. Dropout rate is set to 0.1. For SpecAugment, we set the parameter for time masking T to 40 and that for frequency masking F to 4. The number of time and frequency masks applied m_T and m_F are 2 and 1, respectively.

Evaluation Metrics. For evaluation, we use case-sensitive detokenized SacreBLEU[4] for translation quality evaluation. For latency, we adapt Average Lagging (AL) (Ma et al., 2019) to ST settings, following previous studies (Ma et al., 2020; Zeng et al., 2021). In the submission system, the latency is evaluated with Consecutive Wait (CW) (Gu et al., 2017).

AL in ST evaluates the degree of that the user is out of sync with the speaker, in terms of source speech time duration (Zeng et al., 2021), which is defined as follows:

$$AL(\boldsymbol{x}, \boldsymbol{y}) = \frac{1}{\tau(|\boldsymbol{x}|)} \sum_{i=1}^{\tau(|\boldsymbol{x}|)} [d(y_i) - \frac{|\boldsymbol{x}|}{|\boldsymbol{y}^*|} T_s(i-1)] \quad (7)$$

where $\tau(|\boldsymbol{x}|)$ denotes the target token index when the model has read the entire source speech. $|\boldsymbol{y}^*|$ is the length of the reference translation, and T_s represents that the speech features are extracted

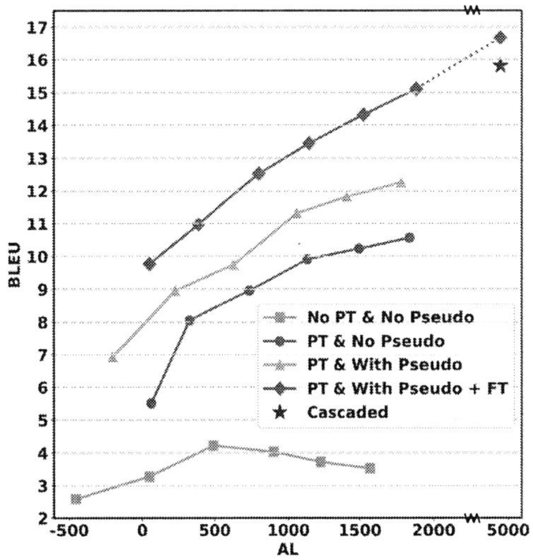

Figure 2: Comparison results of our model variants.

every T_s ms, which will be 80ms in our model. As our acoustic encoder introduces a 100ms look-ahead window, we add 100 to the final AL scores.

CW is the number of source tokens waited between two target tokens, which can be calculated with the following equation (Ma et al., 2019):

$$CW(\boldsymbol{x}, \boldsymbol{y}) = \frac{|\boldsymbol{x}|}{\sum_{i=1}^{|\boldsymbol{y}|} \mathbb{1}_{CW_g(t)>0}} \quad (8)$$

where $\boldsymbol{x}$ here is the corresponding transcription of source speech, and $CW_g(t)$ denotes the waiting source token numbers between time step $t-1$ and t. This means that when evaluated with CW, our model also needs to output transcription. We decide to output the results of CTC greedy paths. In this way, CW can be easily calculated as our wait-k-stride-n policy is applied on the shrunk speech features which are also based on the CTC module.

4.2 Main Results

Figure 2 displays the comparison results among different variants of our model. We compare the following settings:

(a) *No PT & No Pseudo*: We do not use any pretrained modules and directly train the model on the provided in-domain data.

(b) *PT & No Pseudo*: We initialize the model with the pretrained modules and directly train the model on the provided in-domain data.

(c) *PT & With Pseudo*: We initialize the model with the pretrained modules and train the model on the large-scale constructed pseudo data.

(d) *PT & With Pseudo + FT*: We further finetune the model on the in-domain data with multi-domain

[4] https://github.com/mjpost/sacreBLEU

Model	CTC Loss (↓)		BLEU (↑)	
	With Punct	RM Punct	With Punct	RM Punct
No PT & No Pseudo	4.88	4.60	4.12	4.03
FT based on PT + Pseudo	2.10	1.73	11.81	12.41

Table 2: CTC Loss and BLEU results of models trained on in-domain BSTC data, with punctuation preserved or removed. We set the same k ensuring similar latency.

finetuning based on model c.

All of the model variants use wait-k-stride-n simultaneous policy with n=2 and k=2, 4, 6, 8, 10, 12, respectively.

We also compare with the performance of our cascaded model, which first passes the audio input into our pretrained ASR model and then translates with our pretrained NMT model. Since the NMT model is an offline full-sentence translation model, the latency is much higher than the other variants (about 5000ms AL). Therefore, we also compute the offline translation result of our model d for fair comparison.

As can be seen, without any pretraining and extra data, the model performs poorly (model a). With pretraining (model b) and large-scale pseudo data (model c), the model performance increases significantly, which validates the effectiveness of the two training tricks Further finetuning with in-domain data (model d) also introduces reasonable improvement, which shows the importance of domain adaptation. Compared to the cascaded result, our model achieves almost 1 BLEU better than it, indicating the superiority of our RealTranS end-to-end model.

4.3 Further Analysis

Effects of Punctuation Removal. We mainly examine the effects of punctuation removal (only for transcription) during training on the in-domain data. We experiment with two settings. The first one is to directly train on the in-domain data without any pretraining or pseudo data, and the second one is finetuning based on the model with pretraining and pseudo data. We display the results of them with and without punctuation in Table 2.

Both models achieve lower CTC loss values with punctuation removal. It validates that the model can learn better on the acoustic information when punctuation is removed. However, no significant difference is observed in BLEU for the first model while the BLEU is degraded when finetuning the pretrained model with punctuation preserved. It is mainly because the model is first pretrained on the data without punctuation and can be trained more smoothly without punctuation when finetuning.

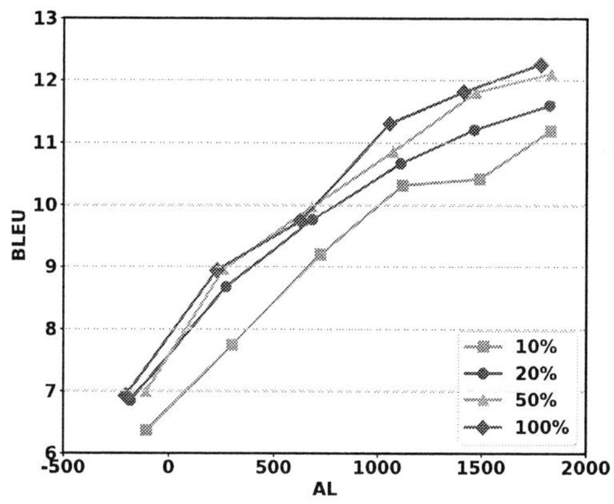

Figure 3: Results of our model when using different amount of pseudo data.

λ value	0.0	0.2	0.4	0.6	0.8	1.0
BLEU	13.07	**13.79**	13.70	13.39	12.53	11.06

Table 3: BLEU scores of models trained with different λ values in Eq. 6. We set the same k ensuring similar latency.

Effects of Pseudo Data Amount. We also want to examine the effects of pseudo data amount during training. We sample 10%, 20% and 50% of our constructed pseudo data and then use them to train our model, respectively. Figure 3 shows the results (before finetuning), together with our model with full data (100%). Comparing models trained with 10% and 20%, it introduces sufficient improvement when doubling the pseudo data. However, when the pseudo data continues to increase, the performance gain becomes smaller, especially for the results in low latency. It is probably because that our NMT model used for generating pseudo translations is trained with limited NMT data (around 9M sentences), much smaller than the used ASR data (around 25M, according to Table 1). The amount of knowledge it carries is not enough to provide such larger amount of efficient pseudo data. Therefore, we might need large amount of data for both recognition and translation to train a more powerful end-to-end ST model.

Effects of Token-level Knowledge Distillation. Our token-level knowledge distillation (KD) from full-sentence NMT model can guide the learning of ST model to forecast target text when the source speech is incomplete during finetuning. We examine the effects of the balance value λ in Eq. 6. The

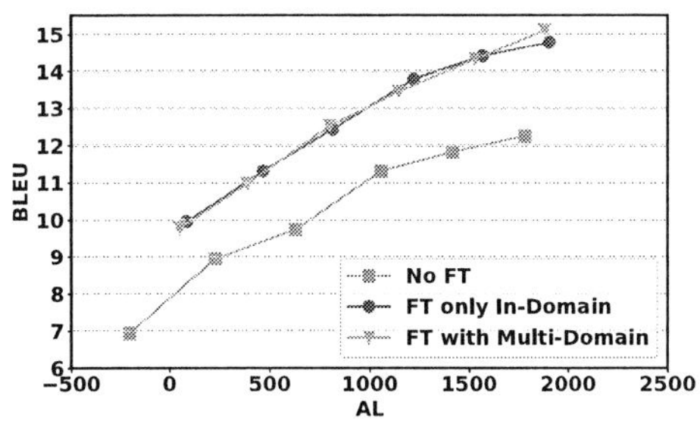

(a) Results in Development Set

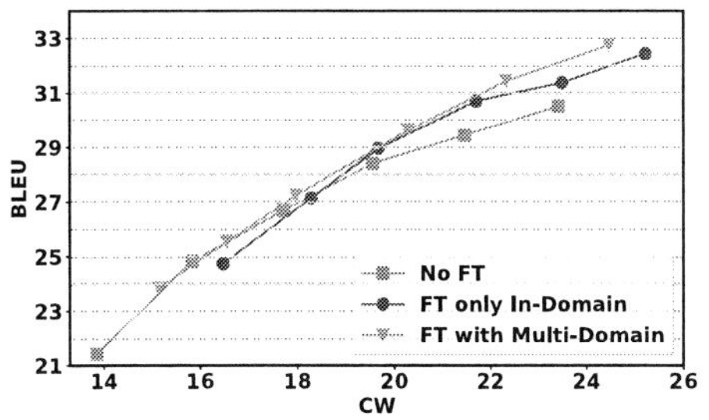

(b) Results in Test Set

Figure 4: Results with different finetuning methods.

results are displayed in Table 3. $\lambda = 0.0$ indicates that no KD is used, and $\lambda = 1.0$ means the model is trained only based on KD but no cross-entropy loss. It can be found that too much guidance from the KD might hurt the performance. We attribute this to two reasons. First, the NMT model is mainly trained with CWMT21 data, which is limited and in a different domain. Second, our model has already been trained with the constructed pseudo data, which can be viewed as another kind of KD (sequence-level KD). Therefore, we choose to select smaller λ (i.e., 0.2) in our experiments.

Effects of Multi-Domain Finetuning. Figure 4 shows the results of our model without finetuning (No FT), only finetuned with in-domain data (FT only In-Domain) and finetuned with multi-domain corpus (FT with Multi-Domain) in the development set and test set, respectively[5]. We can find that though finetuning only with the in-domain data improves a lot in the development set (in average nearly 2 BLEU gain at each latency requirement), the improvement in the test set is limited and performance even hurts at one latency setting (No PT v.s. FT only In-Domain). We attribute this to the fact that the test set may be not exactly in the same domain as the training and development data, and the naive finetuning degrades the ability of domain generalizability. Therefore, we decide to use multi-domain finetuning rather than finetuning only with the in-domain data. As can be seen in Figure 4, this brings no improvement in the development set (FT with Multi-Domain v.s. FT only In-Domain), but improves in the test set.

[5]Note that the test results are validation experiments afterwards and not our submission results.

5 Conclusion

In this work, we describe the details of our submitted system to AutoSimTranS 2022, which won the first place in Chinese-English audio input track. Our model is based on the end-to-end simultaneous speech translation model RealTranS and follows three-step training procedure, including ASR and NMT pretraining, large-scale training on the pseudo data and finetuning on the in-domain data. Our experiments proves the superiority of our model and training procedure and also examines the effectiveness of different techniques like punctuation removal and multi-domain finetuning.

References

Parnia Bahar, Albert Zeyer, Ralf Schlüter, and Hermann Ney. 2019. On using specaugment for end-to-end speech translation. *CoRR*, abs/1911.08876.

Maha Elbayad, Laurent Besacier, and Jakob Verbeek. 2020. Efficient wait-k models for simultaneous machine translation. In *Interspeech 2020, 21st Annual Conference of the International Speech Communication Association, Virtual Event, Shanghai, China, 25-29 October 2020*, pages 1461–1465. ISCA.

Christian Fügen, Alex Waibel, and Muntsin Kolss. 2007. Simultaneous translation of lectures and speeches. *Mach. Transl.*, 21(4):209–252.

Alex Graves, Santiago Fernández, Faustino J. Gomez, and Jürgen Schmidhuber. 2006. Connectionist temporal classification: labelling unsegmented sequence data with recurrent neural networks. In *Machine Learning, Proceedings of the Twenty-Third International Conference (ICML 2006)*, volume 148 of *ACM International Conference Proceeding Series*, pages 369–376. ACM.

Jiatao Gu, Graham Neubig, Kyunghyun Cho, and Victor O.K. Li. 2017. Learning to translate in real-time with neural machine translation. In *Proceedings of the 15th Conference of the European Chapter of the Association for Computational Linguistics: Volume 1, Long Papers*, pages 1053–1062, Valencia, Spain. Association for Computational Linguistics.

Wenyong Huang, Wenchao Hu, Yu Ting Yeung, and Xiao Chen. 2020. Conv-transformer transducer: Low latency, low frame rate, streamable end-to-end speech recognition. In *Interspeech 2020, 21st Annual Conference of the International Speech Communication Association, Virtual Event, Shanghai, China, 25-29 October 2020*, pages 5001–5005. ISCA.

Ye Jia, Melvin Johnson, Wolfgang Macherey, Ron J. Weiss, Yuan Cao, Chung-Cheng Chiu, Naveen Ari, Stella Laurenzo, and Yonghui Wu. 2019. Leveraging weakly supervised data to improve end-to-end speech-to-text translation. In *IEEE International Conference on Acoustics, Speech and Signal Processing, ICASSP 2019, Brighton, United Kingdom, May 12-17, 2019*, pages 7180–7184. IEEE.

Yoon Kim and Alexander M. Rush. 2016. Sequence-level knowledge distillation. In *Proceedings of the 2016 Conference on Empirical Methods in Natural Language Processing*, pages 1317–1327, Austin, Texas. Association for Computational Linguistics.

Diederik P. Kingma and Jimmy Ba. 2015. Adam: A method for stochastic optimization. In *3rd International Conference on Learning Representations, ICLR 2015, San Diego, CA, USA, May 7-9, 2015, Conference Track Proceedings*.

Tom Ko, Vijayaditya Peddinti, Daniel Povey, and Sanjeev Khudanpur. 2015. Audio augmentation for speech recognition. In *INTERSPEECH 2015, 16th Annual Conference of the International Speech Communication Association, Dresden, Germany, September 6-10, 2015*, pages 3586–3589. ISCA.

Taku Kudo and John Richardson. 2018. SentencePiece: A simple and language independent subword tokenizer and detokenizer for neural text processing. In *Proceedings of the 2018 Conference on Empirical Methods in Natural Language Processing: System Demonstrations*, pages 66–71, Brussels, Belgium. Association for Computational Linguistics.

Pengfei Li, Liangyou Li, Meng Zhang, Minghao Wu, and Qun Liu. 2022. Universal conditional masked language pre-training for neural machine translation. *CoRR*, abs/2203.09210.

Xian Li, Changhan Wang, Yun Tang, Chau Tran, Yuqing Tang, Juan Pino, Alexei Baevski, Alexis Conneau, and Michael Auli. 2021. Multilingual speech translation from efficient finetuning of pretrained models. In *Proceedings of the 59th Annual Meeting of the Association for Computational Linguistics and the 11th International Joint Conference on Natural Language Processing (Volume 1: Long Papers)*, pages 827–838, Online. Association for Computational Linguistics.

Mingbo Ma, Liang Huang, Hao Xiong, Renjie Zheng, Kaibo Liu, Baigong Zheng, Chuanqiang Zhang, Zhongjun He, Hairong Liu, Xing Li, Hua Wu, and Haifeng Wang. 2019. STACL: Simultaneous translation with implicit anticipation and controllable latency using prefix-to-prefix framework. In *Proceedings of the 57th Annual Meeting of the Association for Computational Linguistics*, pages 3025–3036, Florence, Italy. Association for Computational Linguistics.

Xutai Ma, Juan Pino, and Philipp Koehn. 2020. SimulMT to SimulST: Adapting simultaneous text translation to end-to-end simultaneous speech translation. In *Proceedings of the 1st Conference of the Asia-Pacific Chapter of the Association for Computational Linguistics and the 10th International Joint Conference on Natural Language Processing*, pages 582–587, Suzhou, China. Association for Computational Linguistics.

Yusuke Oda, Graham Neubig, Sakriani Sakti, Tomoki Toda, and Satoshi Nakamura. 2014. Optimizing segmentation strategies for simultaneous speech translation. In *Proceedings of the 52nd Annual Meeting of the Association for Computational Linguistics (Volume 2: Short Papers)*, pages 551–556, Baltimore, Maryland. Association for Computational Linguistics.

Daniel S. Park, William Chan, Yu Zhang, Chung-Cheng Chiu, Barret Zoph, Ekin D. Cubuk, and Quoc V. Le. 2019. Specaugment: A simple data augmentation method for automatic speech recognition. In *Interspeech 2019, 20th Annual Conference of the International Speech Communication Association, Graz, Austria, 15-19 September 2019*, pages 2613–2617. ISCA.

Sahana Ramnath, Melvin Johnson, Abhirut Gupta, and Aravindan Raghuveer. 2021. Hintedbt: Augmenting back-translation with quality and transliteration hints. In *Proceedings of the 2021 Conference on Empirical Methods in Natural Language Processing, EMNLP 2021, Virtual Event / Punta Cana, Dominican Republic, 7-11 November, 2021*, pages 1717–1733. Association for Computational Linguistics.

Yi Ren, Jinglin Liu, Xu Tan, Chen Zhang, Tao Qin, Zhou Zhao, and Tie-Yan Liu. 2020. SimulSpeech: End-to-end simultaneous speech to text translation. In *Proceedings of the 58th Annual Meeting of the Association for Computational Linguistics*, pages 3787–3796, Online. Association for Computational Linguistics.

Ron J. Weiss, Jan Chorowski, Navdeep Jaitly, Yonghui Wu, and Zhifeng Chen. 2017. Sequence-to-sequence models can directly transcribe foreign speech. *CoRR*, abs/1703.08581.

Chen Xu, Bojie Hu, Yanyang Li, Yuhao Zhang, Shen Huang, Qi Ju, Tong Xiao, and Jingbo Zhu. 2021. Stacked acoustic-and-textual encoding: Integrating the pre-trained models into speech translation encoders. In *Proceedings of the 59th Annual Meeting of the Association for Computational Linguistics and the 11th International Joint Conference on Natural Language Processing (Volume 1: Long Papers)*, pages 2619–2630, Online. Association for Computational Linguistics.

Xingshan Zeng, Liangyou Li, and Qun Liu. 2021. RealTranS: End-to-end simultaneous speech translation with convolutional weighted-shrinking transformer. In *Findings of the Association for Computational Linguistics: ACL-IJCNLP 2021*, pages 2461–2474, Online. Association for Computational Linguistics.

Ruiqing Zhang, Xiyang Wang, Chuanqiang Zhang, Zhongjun He, Hua Wu, Zhi Li, Haifeng Wang, Ying Chen, and Qinfei Li. 2021. BSTC: A large-scale Chinese-English speech translation dataset. In *Proceedings of the Second Workshop on Automatic Simultaneous Translation*, pages 28–35, Online. Association for Computational Linguistics.

Shaolei Zhang and Yang Feng. 2021. ICT's system for AutoSimTrans 2021: Robust char-level simultaneous translation. In *Proceedings of the Second Workshop on Automatic Simultaneous Translation*, pages 1–11, Online. Association for Computational Linguistics.

BIT-Xiaomi's Simultaneous Translation System for AutoSimTrans 2022

Mengge Liu[1*] Xiang Li[2] Bao Chen[1] Yanzhi Tian[1] Tianwei Lan[1]
Silin Li[1] Yuhang Guo[1†] Jian Luan[2] Bin Wang[2]
[1]Beijing Institute of Technology, Beijing, China
[2]Xiaomi AI Lab, Beijing, China
liumengge@bit.edu.cn lixiang21@xiaomi.com
{chenbao,tianyanzhi,lantianwei,lisilin,guoyuhang}@bit.edu.cn
{luanjian,wangbin11}@xiaomi.com

Abstract

This system paper describes the BIT-Xiaomi simultaneous translation system for Autosimtrans 2022 simultaneous translation challenge. We participated in three tracks: the Zh-En text-to-text track, the Zh-En audio-to-text track, and the En-Es test-to-text track. In our system, wait-k is utilized to train prefix-to-prefix translation models. We integrate streaming chunking to detect segmentation boundaries as the source streaming reading in. We further improve our system with data selection, data augmentation, and R-Drop training methods. Results show that our wait-k implementation outperforms the organizer's baseline by at most 8 BLEU score and our proposed streaming chunking method further improves by about 2 BLEU score in the low latency regime.

1 Introduction

Simultaneous translation (Cho and Esipova, 2016; Yarmohammadi et al., 2013; Ma et al., 2019), is a task in Machine Translation (MT), which intends to provide low latency translation in real-time scenarios. To achieve low latency translation, the translation system needs to begin translating before the end of source sentences, which can be viewed as prefix-to-prefix translation (Ma et al., 2019). Simultaneous translation is widely used in real-time translation scenarios such as simultaneous interpretation, online subtitles, and live broadcasting. In these scenarios, low latency may have equal or even higher priority than translation quality.

In simultaneous translation, the most challenge is the balance of translation quality and latency. Low latency translation requires beginning translation with insufficient source information, which may cause incorrect translation results. How to find a simultaneous policy to balance quality and latency is the most challenging question. On another hand, in most cases, the standard machine translation model is trained on full sentences, which can achieve good performance in full-sentence evaluation. But for prefix-to-prefix inference, which is crucial for simultaneous translation, the standard machine translation model always perform poorly.

Previous methods for simultaneous translation can be classified as the fixed policy and the adaptive policy according to different simultaneous policies. Fixed policy uses fixed-latency simultaneous strategy, for example, set value K, and forces the translation to lag behind source for K tokens (Ma et al., 2019). The adaptive policy needs an agent module to perform adaptive simultaneous translation. The agent will consider the current translation state, including the source prefix and the hypothesis prefix, to decide whether to output new tokens at the current state (Gu et al., 2017; Arivazhagan et al., 2019; Ma et al., 2020). Chunk-base (Xiong et al., 2019; Zhang et al., 2020) simultaneous translation is a special adaptive policy, which makes a decision only based on the source prefix.

In our system, we propose a streaming chunking method that can be combined with a fixed wait-k policy. The streaming chunking method can significantly improve translation quality with little latency increase in low latency regions. We train a segmentation model to detect boundaries in streaming sources and employ a wait-k policy to decide output token numbers. We pre-train transformer models with multi-path wait-k on a

*The work was done during the author's internship at Xiaomi.

† Corresponding author.

Proceedings of the Third Workshop on Automatic Simultaneous Translation, pages 34 - 42
July 15-16, 2022 ©2022 Association for Computational Linguistics

Track	Corpus	#Sentence Pairs
Zh-En	BSTC	38K
	CWMT	9M
En-Es	UN Parallel	22M
Zh ASR	BSTC	68h
	AIshell	150h

Table 1: Data statistics. Parallel corpus is counted by sentence pairs. ASR corpus is counted by audio time (hour).

large general corpus and fine-tune with single k on a small domain corpus. We augment the general corpus and domain corpus with Back-Translation (BT) and Front-Translation (FT), and further augment the domain corpus with character-level pseudo ASR error. In training we incorporate R-Drop (liang et al., 2021) method to improve translation quality. In text-to-text tracks, we use text streaming input provided by the organizer. In the audio-to-text track, we train our ASR system to transcript audio into the streaming text as translation input.

The remainder of this paper is organized as follows. We describe the techniques employed in our system and the methods we propose in Section 2. In Section 3 we show our experiment settings and results, including data and model. Finally, we conclude this paper.

2 Methods

In this section, we describe the data, the utilized prefix-to-prefix translation model, and the proposed streaming chunking method.

2.1 Data

We describe the data used in our system from the following aspects: statistics, pre-processing, filtering and data-augmentation.

All allowed bilingual training sets are employed, including the BSTC (Zhang et al., 2021) and the CWMT21 for the Zh-En track, the UN Parallel Corpus for the En-Es track. For the ASR model in the Zh-En audio-to-text track, we use the BSTC and the AIshell (Hui Bu, 2017) corpus for training. Data statistics are shown in Table 1.

Pre-processing. `Sacremoses`[1] is conducted to normalize and tokenize English and Spanish sentences. `Jieba`[2] is used to segment Chinese sentences. And redundant spaces in the text are removed. After tokenization, we apply `Subword-nmt`[3] to learn byte-pair encoding with 32K operations.

Data filtering. The noises in the original data may bring a negative impact on translation quality, so we filter the training set as following steps:

- First, the parallel corpus is filtered by hand-crafted rules. Sentences that contain less than 30% linguistic words will be viewed as noise sentences. When any sentence in a sentence pair is judged as noise, this pair is discarded. For Chinese sentences, we consider Chinese characters as linguistic words. For En or Es, we consider words only containing alphabet characters as linguistic words.

- Second, we utilize `fast_align`[4] to filter out poorly aligned sentence pairs. We calculate align scores for each sentence pair and filter out sentence pairs with low scores. Align score threshold is set as -7.

- Third, language identification is applied with `langid`[5]. Sentences in the wrong languages are viewed as low-quality samples and removed.

- Finally, we discard duplicate pairs and remove the pair with a length ratio greater than 3.0 or the sentence with a length more than 200.

Data selection Because the bilingual corpus utilized in training is not all from the speech domain, we use a language-model-based data selection method select domain data, which is similar to methods proposed by Moore and Lewis (2010). We train two 5-gram language model on source sentences with `KenLM`[6], one on the BSTC corpus (denoted as lm^{in}), another on the CWMT corpus (denoted as lm^{out}). Than for each sentence in the CWMT corpus, we compute the perplexity distances with two language model, which denoted as domain

[1] https://github.com/alvations/sacremoses

[2] https://github.com/fxsjy/jieba

[3] https://github.com/rsennrich/subword-nmt

[4] https://github.com/clab/fast_align

[5] https://github.com/saffsd/langid.py

[6] https://github.com/kpu/kenlm

score for the sentence $ppl\_score = -(ppl^{in} - ppl^{out})$. We sort the corpus by domain score and remove the pair with a large domain distance.

Data augmentation As the training corpus is limited, we utilize back-translation (BT) and front-translation (FT) to augment the training corpus. We first train two translation models in two directions: Zh-En and En-Zh, then generate pseudo training corpus in two directions.

2.2 R-Drop

R-Drop[7] is a method to improve translation quality in machine translation, which can be easily incorporated with our translation model. All models in our system are trained with the R-Drop algorithm proposed by liang et al. (2021).

2.3 Wait-k

Wait-k is a simple and effective method for fixed-policy simultaneous translation, which can train prefix-to-prefix translation ability for transformer models. We build our system based on `fairseq`, which provides a wait-k baseline similar to efficient wait-k (Elbayad et al., 2020). Two-stage training is employed to achieve better performance in the speech domain. Model is firstly trained on large scale parallel corpus with multi-path wait-k, which randomly selects a value of k within the interval (for example, [k, k+n]) for each training batch (denoted as `wait(k)-(k+n)`). Secondly, we fine-tune the model with a small speech domain parallel corpus with simple wait-k (denoted as `wait(k)`) or multi-path wait-k.

2.4 Streaming Chunking

In a streaming translation system, the source is received token by token. The wait-k policy will try to translate each time source is ahead of target for k tokens, which may bring some mistakes when the source stops at a partial phrase. Especially for Chinese streaming input, in which source streaming is growing by character. So some source prefixes may contain incomplete word pieces which may cause misunderstanding and incorrect translation. A stream case with error source prefixes is shown in Table 2. We propose a streaming chunking method, which employs a streaming segmentation model to detect word boundaries on-the-fly in streaming input.

2.4.1 Streaming Segmentation Model

We build our streaming segmentation model base on `chinese-roberta-wwm-ext`[8] proposed by Cui et al. (2021). Compared with a vanilla Chinese word segmentation model, the streaming segmentation model does not need to obtain the complete sentence and can segment words without introducing an additional delay. We treat the streaming word segmentation task as a sequence classification task and use the final hidden state of the classification token ([CLS]) to perform binary classification through a 3-layer fully connected network to determine whether the current source sentence prefix end with complete words. We construct training data using transcribed sentences from the BSTC training set. The complete sentences in the training data are segmented using `pkuseg` (Luo et al., 2019). The source sentence prefixes ending with word boundaries are considered positive examples, while the rest of the source sentence prefixes are negative examples.

2.4.2 Combine with wait-k

We utilize the streaming segmentation model to detect word boundaries and only enable the wait-k policy at the word boundaries to determine word numbers that need to translate. Then the prefix-to-prefix translation is performed, which can avoid translating on source prefix containing incomplete words. Algorithm 1 gives the pseudo code of our proposed method. And Figure 1 shows how the streaming segmentation model works with the wait-k inference.

2.5 Evaluation

We evaluate our simultaneous translation model in two aspects. First is translation quality, we compute BLEU (Papineni et al., 2002) score with merged document translation results. Second, for latency, we utilize Average Lagging (AL) (Ma et al., 2019) to represent the text lagging of our model compared to

[7] https://github.com/dropreg/R-Drop

[8] https://huggingface.co/hfl/chinese-roberta-wwm-ext

stream-id	char-stream	word-stream
1	那	那
2	那首	那
3	那首先	那首先
4	那首先呢	那首先呢
5	那首先呢我	那首先呢我
6	那首先呢我先	那首先呢我先
7	那首先呢我先介	那首先呢我先
8	那首先呢我先介绍	那首先呢我先介绍
9	那首先呢我先介绍一	那首先呢我先介绍
10	那首先呢我先介绍一下	那首先呢我先介绍一下
11	那首先呢我先介绍一下我	那首先呢我先介绍一下我
12	那首先呢我先介绍一下我自	那首先呢我先介绍一下我
13	那首先呢我先介绍一下我自己	那首先呢我先介绍一下我自己
full sentence	nà | shǒu xiān | nē | wǒ | xiān | jiè shào | yí xià | wǒ zì jǐ	
	那 | 首先 | 呢 | 我 | 先 | 介绍 | 一下 | 我自己	
	then | first | - | I | - | introduce | - | myself	

Table 2: Case analysis of incomplete streaming in a Chinese sentence. Char-stream presents sentences by characters. Word-stream presents sentence by word. The prefixes in red color mean error in char-stream, which contains incomplete word-piece. The partial word piece may cause misunderstanding and incorrect translation.

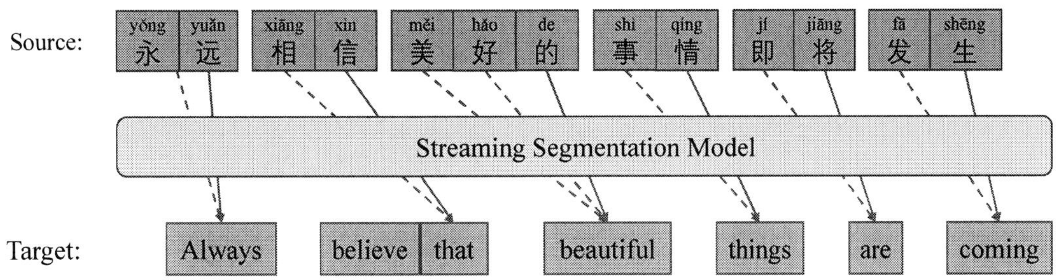

Figure 1: This example shows how the streaming segmentation model works with a wait-k model. The solid lines are the translation points of our proposed method, and the dashed lines are the additional possible translation points of the wait-k model.

Algorithm 1: Wait-k decoding with the streaming chunking method

Input: the translation model M_t, the chunking model M_c, the source sequence x, wait-k lagging K
Output: The translated sentence $\hat{y}$

Initialization: the read token sequence $\hat{x} = []$, the output sentence $\hat{y} = []$,the incomplete word read $x_p = ''$
while $_{|\hat{y}|} \neq$ '</s>' **do**
  if $|\hat{x}| - |\hat{y}| \geq K$ **then**
    $token_{next} = M_t(\hat{x}, \hat{y})$
    $y = y + token_{next}$
  else
    $x_p = x_p + x.next\_char()$
    `// ` x_p ` is a complete word`
    if $M_c(\hat{x}, x_p)$ **then**
      $= + x_p$
      $x_p = ''$
    end
  end
end
return

ideal simultaneous interpretation, which is calculated in the following equation:

$$
\begin{aligned}
AL &= \frac{1}{\tau}\sum_{j=1}^{\tau} g(j) - \frac{j-1}{\gamma} \\
\text{where} \quad \tau &= \arg\min_t [\ g(j) = |X|\ ] \\
\gamma &= |Y|/|X|
\end{aligned}
\tag{1}
$$

3 Experiments and Results

In this section, we describe our experiment settings and results on all the three tracks we participate in.

3.1 Zh-En text-to-text track

For the Zh-En text-to-text track, we introduce our experiments in detail, including model configurations, data, as well as results of a strong wait-k baseline and streaming chunking method.

3.1.1 Model Configurations

In our experiment, we train transformer-big models with the same parameters in Vaswani et al. (2017). The token-level batch size is about 100k on 8 GPUs for pre-training in all experiments. The learning rate is set as 5e-4 for pre-training and 5e-6 for fine-tuning, controlled by Adam optimizer (Kingma and Ba, 2015). We pre-train the model for 100000 steps and save the model every 2000 steps. We fine-tune the model for 10000 steps and save every 200 steps (batch size is about 30k).

3.1.2 Data

We filter the BSTC corpus and the CWMT corpus with methods described in Section 2.1 and apply language-model-based data selection to the CWMT corpus. For the first edition standard transformer model, we mix the BSTC corpus and the CWMT corpus for pre-training, using the BSTC corpus for fine-tuning (denoted as M1). And following is the detail of the M1 model.

For the pre-training stage, we show our results in each filtering step in Table 3. We directly mix the CWMT and the BSTC parallel data as the D0 corpus. The rules-filter discards noise data containing few linguistic words, which improves about 1.3 BLEU. In align-langid-filter, we drop sentence pairs with a align score less than −7 and sentences in the wrong languages. In PPL-selection, we use *ppl_score* computed by the language model to sort sentence pairs and drop sentence pairs with a *ppl_score* larger than 8000. With align-langid-filter and PPL-selection, 1.5M sentence pairs are dropped and nearly no BLEU descend is observed. We get the D1 corpus after all the filtering and selection. Further, we up-sample the BSTC corpus 5 times to enlarge the proportion of domain data. The R-Drop method is incorporated and we choose a larger dropout value (default dropout 0.1). Results in 4 show that the R-Drop ($\alpha = 5$) method significantly improves BLEU, and more increase is observed as we employ these methods together. For fine-tuning, we filter the BSTC corpus by hand-crafted rules and train with the consistent R-Drop method in the pre-training. Finally, we integrate the pre-training and the fine-tuning to train the M1 model, and the performance on the development set is shown in Table 7.

As the training corpus is limited, we utilize data augmentation methods. We perform data augmentation with the M1 model, containing forward-translation (FT) and backward-

Pre-training (data)	Data statistic	dev (SacreBleu)
Orig BSTC+CWMT (D0)	9.1M	16.82
+rules-filter	7.7M	18.09
+align-langid-filter	7.2M	18.04
+PPL-selection (D1)	6.2M	17.99

Table 3: Data filtering and selection in the pre-training stage. BLEU is computed by ScareBleu in sentence-level. Filtering and selection methods are applied incrementally.

Pre-training (method)	Data statistic	dev (SacreBleu)
BSTC+CWMT (D1)	6.2M	17.99
+up-sampling	6.34M	18.40
+dropout 0.25	6.2M	18.59
+R-Drop ($\alpha = 5$)	6.2M	19.72
+up-sampling + dropout 0.25 + R-Drop	6.34M	21.48

Table 4: Data statistic and BLEU on the development of our pre-training methods. BLEU is computed by ScareBleu in sentence-level.

translation (BT) on the pre-training and the fine-tuning corpus. For the pre-training corpus, we leverage the M1 model to perform FT and BT on the D1 corpus, mixed with D1 corpus as the augmented pre-training corpus. Results in Table 5 show FT has better performance than BT. For fine-tuning corpus, we employ the M1 model to translate BSTC corpus in forward and backward paths and add all 5 beam results to the fine-tuning corpus. What's more, to strengthen the robustness of the model, we add char-level augmentation into the fine-tuning corpus, which contains insertion, deletion, duplication, and homophone substitution. For homophone substitution, we use `python-pinyin`[9] to extract homophone dictionary and substitute homophone characters according to character frequency. Results on the fine-tuning corpus are shown in Table 6, which indicates that each augmentation method is useful.

Finally, we add FT augmentation in pre-training, add FT, and BT as well as character augmentation in fine-tuning. The model trained with augmented pre-training and fine-tuning is denoted as the M2 models. Significant improvement of the M2 model against the M1 model could be observed in Table 7.

3.1.3 Wait-k Baseline

To improve prefix-to-prefix translation quality, we use wait-k training described in Section 2.3. Using the same training data of the M2 model, we pre-train the model with multi-path wait-k and fine-tune with simple wait-k or multi-path wait-k. We report the results of our model on the BSTC development set. All trained model is listed in Table 8, and we show the AL-BLEU curve of several models. We achieve good performance according to Figure 2, in which our `M2_wait1-9_wait5` model exceeds the PaddlePaddle wait-5 model by at most 8 BLEU. The model trained with small k may achieve better performance in the low-latency regime, but not perform well in the high-latency regime. What's more, we ensemble the top-3 model in each inference k, which shows benefits across all latency regimes. Same as Guo et al. (2022), standard beam-search is utilized after the source stream is finished. Our models achieve almost consistent performance in high latency regime.

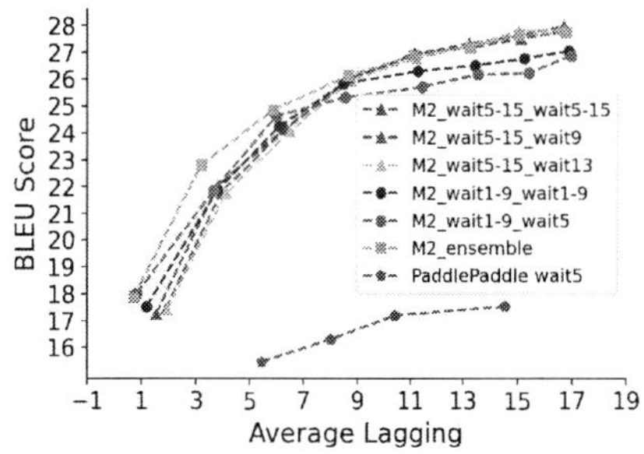

Figure 2: Results of M2 wait-k models. Models are list in Table 8. PaddlePaddle_wait5 is wait-k model provided by organizer.

[9] https://github.com/mozillazg/python-pinyin

Pre-training (Augmentation)	Data statistic (Pre-training)	dev (SacreBleu)
M1 (only pre-train)	6.34M	21.48
+FT pre-train	10.95M	22.32
+BT pre-train	11.03M	19.90

Table 5: Results of data augmentation in the pre-training stage. We use the M1 model to generate the FT and BT augment data and mixed with the D1 corpus for pre-training.

Fine-tuning (Augmentation)	Data statistic (Fine-tuning)	dev (SacreBleu)
M1 (fine-tuned on BSTC)	36K	22.41
+5FT	197K	22.92
+5BT	211K	22.59
+char-aug	185K	22.80
+5BT +5FT +char-aug	525K	23.05

Table 6: Results of data augmentation in the fine-tuning stage. The M1 model is leveraged to generate FT and BT augment data, and beam 5 results are saved. For the char-aug, we use character-level augmentations including insertion, deletion, duplication, and homophone substitution. The models in this table are all based on the same pre-trained model.

Model	dev (SacreBleu)	dev (Mteval-v13a)
M1	22.43	27.26
M2	23.62	28.96

Table 7: Results of data augmentation on standard transformer model. The M1 model is trained with pre-training and fine-tuning. The M2 model leverage data augmentation in both the pre-training and the fine-tuning stage.

Model name	Pre-train	Fine-tune
M2_wait5-15_wait5	$K \in [5, 15]$	$K = 5$
M2_wait5-15_wait7	$K \in [5, 15]$	$K = 7$
M2_wait5-15_wait9	$K \in [5, 15]$	$K = 9$
M2_wait5-15_wait11	$K \in [5, 15]$	$K = 11$
M2_wait5-15_wait13	$K \in [5, 15]$	$K = 13$
M2_wait5-15_wait15	$K \in [5, 15]$	$K = 15$
M2_wait5-15_wait5-15	$K \in [5, 15]$	$K \in [5, 15]$
M2_wait1-9_wait1	$K \in [1, 9]$	$K = 1$
M2_wait1-9_wait3	$K \in [1, 9]$	$K = 3$
M2_wait1-9_wait5	$K \in [1, 9]$	$K = 5$
M2_wait1-9_wait1-9	$K \in [1, 9]$	$K \in [1, 9]$

Table 8: Our wait-k models are pre-trained and fine-tuned on the same data of the M2 model in Section 3.1. We show the K value settings in pre-training and fine-tuning wait-k training for all M2 wait-k models. Take M2_wait5-15_wait5 for example, we use multi-path wait-k training with $K \in [5, 15]$ for pre-training and use simple wait-k with $K = 5$ for fine-tuning.

3.1.4 Streaming Chunking

In this section, we add streaming chunking methods. We first fine-tune our segmentation model based on `chinese-roberta-wwm-ext` on BSTC train set and get 92.0% accuracy and 93.7% F-score on the BSTC development set. Then we employ our segmentation to perform online source chunking to detect word boundaries. The results in Figure 3 show about 2 BLEU improvements in the low-latency regime with a little increase in AL.

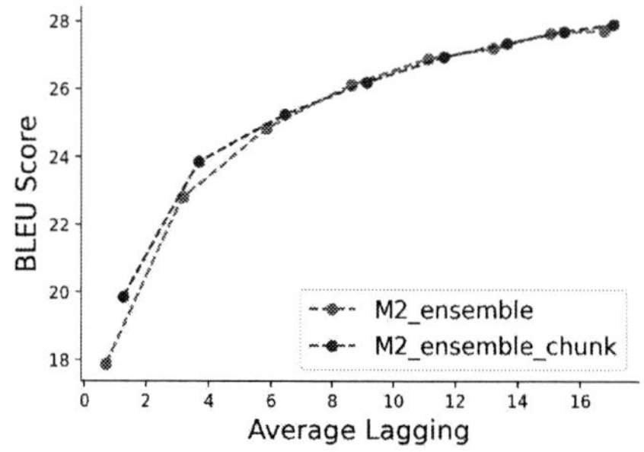

Figure 3: Results of streaming chunking method. M2_ensemble_chunk add streaming segmentation model compare to M2_ensemble.

3.2 En-Es text-to-text track

For En-Es text-to-text track, we use the same data filtering rules on the UN-parallel corpus. Because of lacking speech corpus, we didn't perform data selection and augmentation. Standard and wait1-11 transformers are trained and we report our results on the development set in Figure 4.

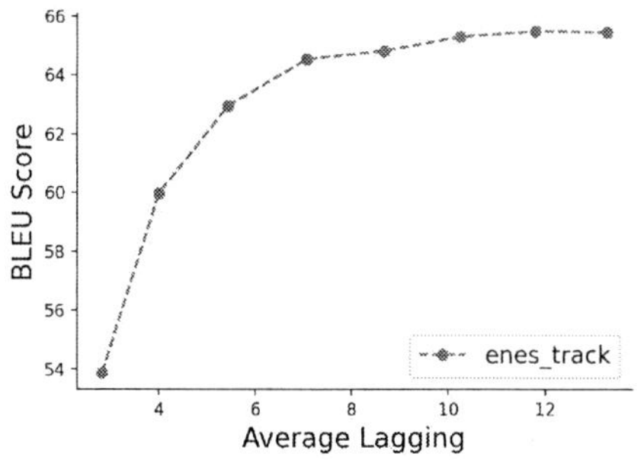

Figure 4: Results of En-Es text-to-text track. BLEU is computed in document level with Mteval-v13a.

3.3 Zh-En audio-to-text track

In Zh-En audio-to-text track, we train a simple transformer ASR model[10] with audio from BSTC and AIshell. The audio wav files are segmented by Silero-VAD(Team, 2021) and we achieve 0.38 WER on development and 0.28 WER on the test. And we perform simultaneous decoding on the ASR transcriptions with the same model and settings in the text-to-text track. Results show on development Figure 5 shows that the translation BLEU dropped by about 10 BLEU on audio input.

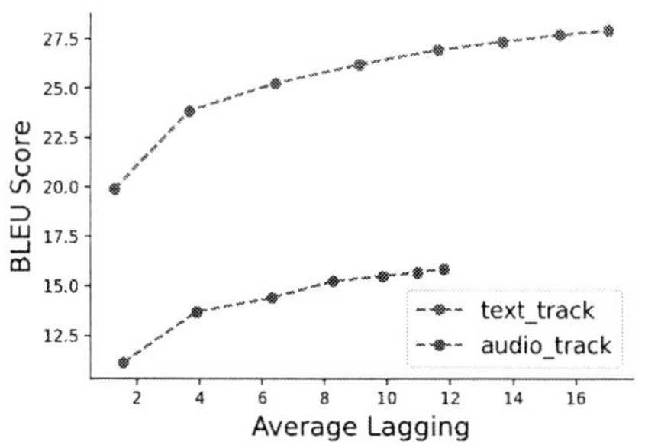

Figure 5: Results of Zh-En audio-to-text track. BLEU is computed in document level with Mteval-v13a.

4 Conclusion

We elaborate on the BIT-Xiaomi simultaneous translation system in this paper. We investigate data filtering and augmentation to enlarge high-quality corpus and utilize the R-Drop method to improve translation quality. We train our simultaneous translation models based on the wait-k strategy, and the streaming chunking method is employed to avoid segmentation errors in the source stream. The results on Zh-En text-to-text track indicate that the streaming chunking method can be integrated with the streaming decoding and improves translation quality. The slightly worse quality on the audio track suggests that the ASR error may affect translation quality much. In the future, we will explore better streaming ASR models and try more interesting simultaneous policies to get better latency and quality.

[10]https://github.com/facebookresearch/fairseq/blob/main/examples/speech_to_text/docs/mustc_example.md

Acknowledgements

This work is supported by the National Key RD Program of China (No. 2020AAA0106600).

References

Naveen Arivazhagan, Colin Cherry, Wolfgang Macherey, Chung-Cheng Chiu, Semih Yavuz, Ruoming Pang, Wei Li, and Colin Raffel. 2019. Monotonic infinite lookback attention for simultaneous machine translation. In *Proc. of ACL*.

Kyunghyun Cho and Masha Esipova. 2016. Can neural machine translation do simultaneous translation? *arXiv preprint arXiv:1606.02012*.

Yiming Cui, Wanxiang Che, Ting Liu, Bing Qin, Ziqing Yang, Shijin Wang, and Guoping Hu. 2021. Pre-training with whole word masking for chinese bert. *IEEE/ACM Transactions on Audio, Speech, and Language Processing*.

Maha Elbayad, Laurent Besacier, and Jakob Verbeek. 2020. Efficient Wait-k Models for Simultaneous Machine Translation. In *Proc. of Interspeech*.

Jiatao Gu, Graham Neubig, Kyunghyun Cho, and Victor O.K. Li. 2017. Learning to translate in real-time with neural machine translation. In *Proc. of EACL*.

Bao Guo, Mengge Liu, Wen Zhang, Hexuan Chen, Chang Mu, Xiang Li, Jianwei Cui, Bin Wang, and Yuhang Guo. 2022. The xiaomi text-to-text simultaneous speech translation system for IWSLT 2022. In *Proceedings of the 19th International Conference on Spoken Language Translation (IWSLT 2022)*.

Xingyu Na Bengu Wu Hao Zheng Hui Bu, Jiayu Du. 2017. Aishell-1: An open-source mandarin speech corpus and a speech recognition baseline. In *Oriental COCOSDA 2017*.

Diederick P Kingma and Jimmy Ba. 2015. Adam: A method for stochastic optimization. In *Proc. of ICLR*.

xiaobo liang, Lijun Wu, Juntao Li, Yue Wang, Qi Meng, Tao Qin, Wei Chen, Min Zhang, and Tie-Yan Liu. 2021. R-drop: Regularized dropout for neural networks. In *Proc. of NeurIPS*.

Ruixuan Luo, Jingjing Xu, Yi Zhang, Xuancheng Ren, and Xu Sun. 2019. Pkuseg: A toolkit for multi-domain chinese word segmentation. *CoRR*.

Mingbo Ma, Liang Huang, Hao Xiong, Renjie Zheng, Kaibo Liu, Baigong Zheng, Chuanqiang Zhang, Zhongjun He, Hairong Liu, Xing Li, Hua Wu, and Haifeng Wang. 2019. STACL: Simultaneous translation with implicit anticipation and controllable latency using prefix-to-prefix framework. In *Proc. of ACL*.

Xutai Ma, Juan Miguel Pino, James Cross, Liezl Puzon, and Jiatao Gu. 2020. Monotonic multihead attention. In *Proc. of ICLR*.

Robert C Moore and William Lewis. 2010. Intelligent selection of language model training data. In *Proceedings of the ACL 2010 conference short papers*.

Kishore Papineni, Salim Roukos, Todd Ward, and Wei-Jing Zhu. 2002. Bleu: a method for automatic evaluation of machine translation. In *Proc. of ACL*.

Silero Team. 2021. Silero vad: pre-trained enterprise-grade voice activity detector (vad), number detector and language classifier.

Ashish Vaswani, Noam Shazeer, Niki Parmar, Jakob Uszkoreit, Llion Jones, Aidan N Gomez, Łukasz Kaiser, and Illia Polosukhin. 2017. Attention is all you need. *Proc. of NeurIPS*.

Hao Xiong, Ruiqing Zhang, Chuanqiang Zhang, Zhongjun He, Hua Wu, and Haifeng Wang. 2019. Dutongchuan: Context-aware translation model for simultaneous interpreting. *arXiv preprint arXiv:1907.12984*.

Mahsa Yarmohammadi, Vivek Kumar Rangarajan Sridhar, Srinivas Bangalore, and Baskaran Sankaran. 2013. Incremental segmentation and decoding strategies for simultaneous translation. In *Proceedings of the Sixth International Joint Conference on Natural Language Processing*.

Ruiqing Zhang, Xiyang Wang, Chuanqiang Zhang, Zhongjun He, Hua Wu, Zhi Li, Haifeng Wang, Ying Chen, and Qinfei Li. 2021. BSTC: A large-scale Chinese-English speech translation dataset. In *Proceedings of the Second Workshop on Automatic Simultaneous Translation*.

Ruiqing Zhang, Chuanqiang Zhang, Zhongjun He, Hua Wu, and Haifeng Wang. 2020. Learning adaptive segmentation policy for simultaneous translation. In *Proc. of EMNLP*.

USST's System for AutoSimTrans 2022

Jiahui Zhu [1] and **Jun Yu** [2]
[1] Shanghai University of Science and Technology
[2] East China University of Science and Technology
Shanghai, China
[1] zhujiahui.cn@outlook.com, [2] y45190321@mail.ecust.edu.cn

Abstract

This paper describes our submitted text-to-text Simultaneous translation (ST) system, which won the second place in the Chinese→English streaming translation task of AutoSimTrans 2022. Our baseline system is a BPE-based Transformer model trained with the PaddlePaddle framework. In our experiments, we employ data synthesis and ensemble approaches to enhance the base model. In order to bridge the gap between general domain and spoken domain, we select in-domain data from a general corpus and mix them with a spoken corpus for mixed fine-tuning. Finally, we adopt a fixed wait-k policy to transfer our full-sentence translation model to simultaneous translation model. Experiments on the development data show that our system outperforms the baseline system.

1 Introduction

Simultaneous translation (Gu et al., 2017; Ma et al., 2018) consists in generating a translation before the source speaker finishes speaking. It is widely used in many real-time scenarios such as international conferences, business negotiations and legal proceedings. The challenge of Simultaneous machine translation is to find a read-write policy that balances translation quality and latency. The translation quality will decline if the machine translation system reads insufficient source information. When reading wider source text, latency will increase.

Recent read-write policies can be divided into two categories: fixed policies such as wait-k (Ma et al., 2018), wait-if* (Cho and Esipova, 2016), and adaptive policies such as MoChA (Chiu and Raffel, 2017), MILk (Arivazhagan et al., 2019) and MU (Zhang et al., 2020). Fixed policies are simple to implement, but they neglect contextual information, which might result in quality reduction. Dynamic policies are more flexible, they can learn from data to achieve better quality/latency trade-offs, but accordingly difficult to train.

In our system, we train a Transformer (Vaswani et al., 2017) with a deep encoder (Meng et al., 2020) as baseline for abtaining rich source representations, besides we initialize the model with the method mentioned in DeepNet (Wang et al., 2022) in order to stabilize the training of the deeper model. At the pre-training stage, we firstly pretrain our model on a large general corpus, then we utilize data synthesis methods such as self-training and back-translation to improve model quality.

During the fine-tuning phase, we first apply finetuning on a small spoken corpus. For better domain adaptation, we adopt mixed fine-tuning (Chu et al., 2017), which trains on a mixed dataset that includes a subsampled general corpus and an upsampled spoken corpus. Thirdly, we propose a method called "in-domain mixed fine-tuning", which further improve the BLEU score than mixed finetuning. Specifically, inspired by in-domain data filtering (Moore and Lewis, 2010; Ng et al., 2019), we mixed upsampled spoken data with selected in-domain data from general corpus rather than random subsampled.

In the final stage, we employ the wait-k policy to convert the full-sentence translation model into a prefix-to-prefix architecture that predicts target words with only the source sentence's prefixes. After waiting for k-1 source subwords, the system reads a source subword and then predicts a target subword alternately until <eos> is detected. An example of wait 1 is shown in Figure 1.

The contributions of this paper are as follows:

- We propose a domain adaption approach called "in-domain mixed fine-tuning", which empirically proved to be better than finetuning while mitigating overfitting.
- All our code has been open sourced, see USST[1].

[1] https://github.com/tyy2022/USST_AutoSimultrans2022

Proceedings of the Third Workshop on Automatic Simultaneous Translation, pages 43 - 49
July 15-16, 2022 ©2022 Association for Computational Linguistics

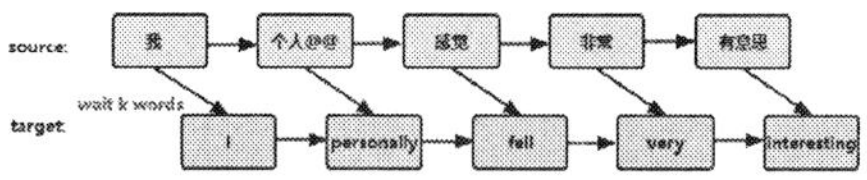

Figure 1: An example of prefix-to-prefix (wait 1).

2 Data

We participate in the Chinese-English streaming transcription track , where each sentence is broken into lines whose length is incremented by one word until the sentence is completed. An example is shown in Table 1.

Streaming transcription	Translation
我	
我下	I
我下面	
我下面来	'm
我下面来讲	
我下面来讲我	going
我下面来讲我们	
我下面来讲我们这	to
我下面来讲我们这段	talk
我下面来讲我们这段故	
我下面来讲我们这段故事	about
我下面来讲我们这段故事。	this story.

Table 1: An example of streaming input and output.

For pre-training, we use the CWMT21 parallel corpus (9.1M) [2], and we fine-tune the pre-trained model using transcription and translation of the BSTC (Baidu Speech Translation Corpus,37K) (Zhang et al., 2021), shown in Table 2. We also use CWMT's 10M Chinese monolingual data for synthetic data generation.

Similar to (Ng et al., 2019; Meng et al., 2020), we preprocess the data as follows:

- Word Segmentation: For Chinese, we use the open-source Chinese word segmentation tool jieba [3] for word segmentation. For English, we adopt punctuation-normalization, tokenization and truecasing with Moses scripts[4].
- Length filter: We remove sentences that are longer than 250 words and sentence pairs with a source/target length ratio exceeding 2.5.
- Langage identification (langid) (Lui and Baldwin, 2012): We use fastText[5] for language identification filtering, which removes sentence pairs that are not predicted as the correct language on either side.
- Deduplication: Remove duplicate sentences in Chinese monolingual data.
- Byte-pair-encoding (BPE) (Sennrich et al., 2016)[6]: For both the Chinese and English sides, we use BPE with 32K operations.

See Table 3 for details on the filtered data size.

Datasets	Domain	Train size	Dev size
CWMT21	General	9,023,708	1011
BSTC	Spoken	37,901	956

Table 2: Statistics of Chinese→English parallel corpus.

	Zh-En	Zh Mono
no filter	9.1M	10M
+length filter	8.9M	10M
+langid filter	8.8M	10M
+deduplication	-	6.8M

Table 3: Number of sentences in bitext and mono datasets for different filtering scheme

3 System Overview

3.1 Baseline System

As shown in previous work (Wang et al., 2019; Sun et al., 2019; Meng et al., 2020), increasing the depth of the Transformer encoder can substantially improve model performance, therefore we train the Transformer with deep encoder to obtain a better source representation.

In addition, in order to have both the high performance of post-norm and the stable training of pre-norm (Nguyen and Salazar, 2019), we use the methods mentioned in DeepNet (Wang et al., 2022), including a normalization function deepnorm that modifies the residual connection and a theoretically derived initialization. Our model configurations are shown in Table 4.

[2] http://mteval.cipsc.org.cn:81/agreement/AutoSimTrans

[3] https://github.com/fxsjy/jieba

[4] https://github.com/moses-smt/mosesdecoder

[5] https://github.com/facebookresearch/fastText

[6] https://github.com/rsennrich/subword-nmt

Configuration	Value
Encoder depth	12
Decoder depth	6
Attention heads	8
Embedding dim	512
FFN size	2048
Chinese vocab size	45942
English vocab size	32151
dropout	0.1

Table 4: Model Configuration

For training the full-sentence translation model, given the source sentence x, the probability of predicting the target sentence y is as shown in Eq. 1, and the training objective is to minimize the negative log-likelihood as shown in Eq. 2.

$$p(y|x) = \prod_{t=1}^{|y|} p(y_t|x, y_{<t}; \theta) \tag{1}$$

$$loss_{full}(\theta) = -\sum_{(x,y)\in D} log p_g(y|x;\theta) \tag{2}$$

The batch size for training is 4,096 tokens per GPU, and we trained our model for 7 epochs on 4 NVIDIA V100 GPUs for about 10 hours.

3.2 Data Synthesis

In order to improve the model performance, we used self-training and back-translation to synthesize pseudo-parallel corpus. Before using the two methods, we averaged 3 best checkpoints.

Self-training (He et al., 2019; Chen et al., 2020) uses a source-to-target model to generate synthetic pairs from source-side monolingual data to augment the original parallel corpus. We combined 2M Chinese monolingual data with 2M Chinese sentences randomly sampled from the CWMT parallel corpus, yielding a total of 4M monolingual for forward translation.

Reversely, back-translation (Sennrich et al., 2015; Edunov et al., 2018) first trains a target-to-source model, which then utilizes target-side monolingual data to synthesis a pseudo-parallel corpus. We randomly select 2M English sentences from the CWMT parallel corpus for back-translation.

We set the beam size to 5 for data generation, and then filtered out sentence pairs with normalized log score less than -3, resulting in a total of 5.7M pseudo-parallel sentences. Finally, we combined the pseudo corpus and the CWMT corpus to get a total of 14.5M sentences, and continued to train the forward model for 2 epochs, for about 2.5 hours on 4 V100 GPUSs.

3.3 Domain Adaption

A simple yet effective method for improving translation quality on the downstream task is fine-tuning with domain data,which is known as domain adaption (Luong and Manning, 2015). We train for another 2 epochs on the BSTC dataset with pre-trained model. Furthermore, we obverse that fine-tuning on limited spoken corpus lead to overfit quickly, as evidenced by the significant improvement on the BSTC development set while degrades rapidly on the CWMT development set.

In order to solve this issue, we explored mixed fine-tuning, an advanced domain adaption method that fine tunes a pre-trained model on a mixed corpus of in-domain and out-domain corpora. In addition, domain tags are added to all corpora to denote specific domains. In our experiments, we randomly sample 0.1M corpus from CWMT and upsample BSTC to 0.1M, then mix them up and shuffle randomly as for training set. For development set, we directly use the development set of BSTC rather than mixing in-domain and out-of-domain development sets.

We also verified the domain tags' efficacy and placement, the results show that appending the domain tags to source sentence performs best. However, in simultaneous translation task, this is unacceptable since the prefix-to-prefix model will not see the tag at the beginning.

To address this problem, we identify a 0.1M subset of CWMT that is most similar to BSTC by in-domain data filtering, then mixed the subset with upsampled 0.1M BSTC data. On the one hand, mixing increases the amount of domain data. On the other hand, there is no need to add tags because the mixed data only contains spoken domain.

For in-domain data filtering, given an in-domain data I, in this case BSTC, and a non-domain specific data N, in this case CWMT, we want to find the subset N_I that is drawn from the same distribution as I. Using Bayes' rule, we can calculate the probability that sentences in N is drawn from N_I for any given sentences, as shown in Eq. 3.

$$P(N_I|s, N) = \frac{P(s|N_I)P(N_I|N)}{P(s|N)} \tag{3}$$

$$logP(N_I|s, N) = logP(s|I) - logP(s|N) \tag{4}$$

Because I and N_I are drawn from the same distribution, we use $P(s|I)$ instead of $P(s|N_I)$. Besides, we neglect the $P(N_I|N)$ term because it will be constant for any given I and N.

Equivalently, in the log domain, the score of a sentence can be calculated as Eq. 4. This is similar to working with the cross-entropy difference: $H_I(s) - H_N(s)$, where $H_I(s)$ and $H_N(s)$ are the length-normalized cross entropy scores for a sentence s according to language models L_I and L_N.

$$Score(p)_{abs} = |P_I(p) - P_N(p)| \quad (5)$$

$$Score(p)_{noabs} = P_I(p) - P_N(p) \quad (6)$$

For simplicity, in this paper, we replace the monolingual sentence s with the sentence pair p drawn from non-domain corpus, the n-gram language model with Neural Machine Translation (NMT) model, the cross-entropy difference with perplexity absolute difference, as shown in Eq. 5, where $P_N(p)$ and $P_I(p)$ are the perplexity scores for a sentence pair p using an non-domain NMT_N model (pre-trained on CWMT) and an in-domain NMT_I model (fine-tuned on BSTC), respectively. We extracted 2M corpus from CWMT to calculate the absolute difference of perplexity scores, and screened 0.1M sentence pairs with the lowest scores, or about 5% of extracted data. We also tried to use the perplexity difference (see Eq. 6).

3.4 Ensemble

Averaging checkpoints is an easy but powerful ensemble method. We performed in-domain mix fine-tuning twice with two different random seeds, each taking the highest BLEU score checkpoint on the BSTC development set (up to 0.6 BLEU improvements).

System	BLEU	AL
pre-train	19.04	24.38
FT	25.11	24.35
In MF (abs)	26.35	24.33
+ensemble	**26.96**	24.34

Table 5: BLEU and Average Lagging on BSTC dev set. ("MF": Mixed fine-tuning)

3.5 Wait-k

The wait-k policy (Ma et al., 2018) refers to write target word y_t after reading source-side prefix $(x_1..x_{t+k-1})$. Let $g(t)$ be a monotonic non-decreasing function of t that indicates the number of source words read by the encoder when writing the target word y_t. Unlike full-sentence translation, the wait-k policy uses the source prefix $(x_1, \ldots, x_{g(t)})$ rather than the whole sentence x to generate y_t: $p(y_t|x_{\leq g(t)}, y_{<t})$. Thus, the decoding probability is shown in Eq. 7, and given training data D, the training objective is shown in Eq. 8.

$$p_g(y|x) = \prod_{t=1}^{|y|} p(y_t|x_{\leq g(t)}, y_{<t}; \theta) \quad (7)$$

$$loss_g(\theta) = - \sum_{(x,y)\in D} logp_g(y|x; \theta) \quad (8)$$

For k=1,3,5,7 we train 600 steps, and 300 steps for k=9 on the BSTC training set. Training more steps causes reduction of BLEU on the BSTC development set.

4 Experiments

Our system is implemented with the PaddlePaddle[7] framework, and our experiments are carried out on AI Studio[8] with 4 NVIDIA V100 GPU each of which has 32 GB memory. (We also benchmarked our code against fairseq [9], see Appendix A)

4.1 Settings

For all experiments, we use the Adam optimizer with $\beta 1 = 0.9$, $\beta 2 = 0.98$. The initial learning rate is 1e-7, grows linearly to peak, then decayed proportionally to the inverse square root of the step number. During the training phase, we set peak learning rate to 5e-4, warmup step= 4000, max tokens= 4096, and update frequency = 4. Label smoothing with 0.1 is also adopted. The specific training parameters are shown in Table 7. We set beam size to 5 and length penalty to 1 during decoding.

4.2 Post-processing

For the post-processing after wait-k decoding, we apply de-truecaseing and de-tokenizing on the English translations with the scripts given in Moses.

[7] https://github.com/PaddlePaddle

[8] https://aistudio.baidu.com/aistudio/index

[9] https://github.com/facebookresearch/fairseq

System	CWMT Dev	BSTC Dev
Pre-train	27.39	16.93
+Fine-tuning	22.24	**20.46**
Self-training + Back-translation	**28.77**	16.55
+Fine-tuning	22.14	20.13
MF w/o tags	24.54	20.13
MF train tags(→)	24.74	19.23
MF train/test tags(→)	24.46	**20.86**
MF train tags(←)	**24.99**	19.60
MF train/test tags(←)	24.57	20.31
In MF (abs)	24.47	21.47
+ ensemble	**24.91**	**21.75**
In MF (no abs)	24.05	21.14

Table 6: Translation quality of our Chinese→English system. ("MF": Mixed fine-tuning; "w/o tags": With out tags; "train tags": Only add tags to the training set; "train/test tags": Add tags to both the training and test set; "→/←": Refers to whether to append or prepend tags to source text; "In MF": In-domain Mixed fine-tuning.)

Parameter	Pre-train	Fine-tune	Wait-k
Learning rate	5e-4	5e-5	5e-5
Warmup step	4000	500	500
Max tokens	4096	4096	512
Update frequency	4	1	1
Training time	7e	2e	600s

Table 7: Traing parameters. ("e": Epoch number; "s": Step number.)

4.3 Evaluation Metric

We use BLEU (Papineni et al., 2002) [10] and Average Lagging (AL) (Ma et al., 2018) [11] to evaluate translation quality and latency respectively. AL measures the degree the user is out of sync with the speaker. As shown in Eq.9-10, t is decoding step, τ is cut-off decoding step where source sentence is finished, $g(t)$ denotes the number of source words read by the encoder at decoding step t, and $r = |x|/|y|$ is the target-to-source length ratio. The smaller the AL (roughly equivalent to k) is, the more real-time the simultaneous translation system is.

$$AL_g(x, y) = \frac{1}{\tau}\sum_{t=1}^{\tau} g(t) - \frac{t-1}{r} \tag{9}$$

$$where\ \tau_g(|x|) = \min\{t|g(t) = |x|\} \tag{10}$$

4.4 Results and Analysis

Table 6 shows the translation quality variation of our system on the validation sets of CWMT and BSTC. The fine-tuning resulted in a significant improvement of 3.5 BLEU on BSTC, while dropping rapidly on CWMT with 5.1 BLEU. We observe that although using self-training and back-translation improves CWMT by 1.3 BLEU, it decreases by 0.4 BLEU on BSTC. This may be overfitting on the general domain and further deviating from the spoken domain. So in the later experiments, we directly use the pre-trained model to continue fine-tuning.

Lines 5–9 depict the mixed fine-tuning discussed in Section 3.3. We experimented with whether and where to add a tag, and discovered that adding tag at the end of source text works best, which is in line with the original paper's conclusion. The mixed fine-tuning reached 20.86 BLEU, a 0.4 BLEU improvement over the fine-tuning.

Finally, the in-domain mixed fine-tuning proposed in this paper is 0.6 BLEU better than mixed-fine-tuning, and after averaging two checkpoints, it further improved by 0.3 points to 21.75 BLEU, which is 1.3 BLEU higher than fine-tuning. In addition, we attempted to select the in-domain data using the perplexity difference (last row of Table 6, corresponding to Eq. 6), but the experimental re-

[10] https://dataset-bj.cdn.bcebos.com/qianyan/AST_Challenge.zip

[11] https://github.com/autosimtrans/SimulTransBaseline/blob/master/latency.py

sults proved to be less effective than the absolute value of the perplexity difference.

Table 5 and Figure 2 illustrates the translation quality and latency results after wait-k training. We set k=1, 3, 5, 7, 9, and train 600 steps until the training perplexity starts to rise. We only plot the results of using ensemble checkpoint for wait-k training since the effect of using in-domain mixed fine-tuning does not significantly exceed fine-tune when using wait-k training.

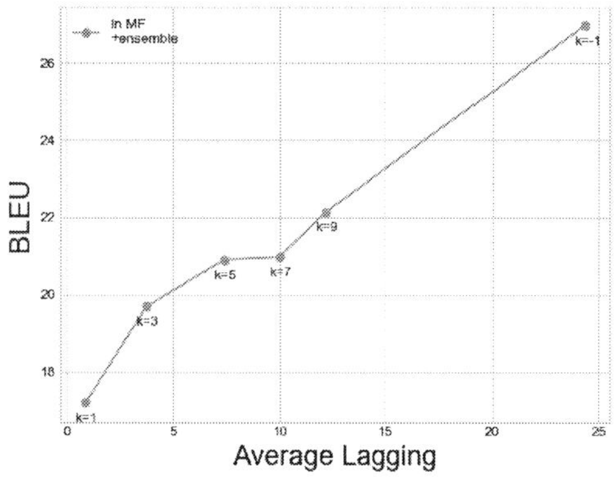

Figure 2: Translation quality (BLEU) against latency metric (AL) on Chinese→English (BSTC) simultaneous translation, showing the results of wait-k and full-sentences (k=-1) of the offline system. "In MF +ensemble" means using averaged checkpoints of the In-domain Mixed fine-tuning to perform wait-k training.

5 Conclusion

In this paper we describe our Chinese-to-English simultaneous translation system, which uses a deep Transformer to improve translation quality and adopts wait-k policy (Ma et al., 2018) to reduce latency. Besides, for better domain adaption, we combined mixed fine-tuning (Chu et al., 2017) with in-domain data filtering (Moore and Lewis, 2010; Ng et al., 2019) and proposed a new domain adaption method called "in-domain mixed fine-tuning", which is empirically more effective than fine-tuning and mixed fine-tuning.

In our future work, we plan to validate the effective of our proposed in-domain mixed fine-tuning on more datasets, while investigating some novel domain adaption methods. We also plan to research on some dynamic read-write policies in order to better balance quality and latency for simultaneous translation tasks.

Acknowledgements

This work was supported by Baidu's AI Studio, thanks to its free computing resources, and we sincerely hope that the PaddlePaddle framework will be built better. We also thank all the anonymous reviewers for their insightful and valuable comments.

References

Naveen Arivazhagan, Colin Cherry, Wolfgang Macherey, Chung-Cheng Chiu, Semih Yavuz, Ruoming Pang, Wei Li, and Colin Raffel. 2019. Monotonic infinite lookback attention for simultaneous machine translation. *arXiv preprint arXiv:1906.05218*.

Peng-Jen Chen, Ann Lee, Changhan Wang, Naman Goyal, Angela Fan, Mary Williamson, and Jiatao Gu. 2020. Facebook ai's wmt20 news translation task submission. *arXiv preprint arXiv:2011.08298*.

Chung-Cheng Chiu and Colin Raffel. 2017. Monotonic chunkwise attention. *arXiv preprint arXiv:1712.05382*.

Kyunghyun Cho and Masha Esipova. 2016. Can neural machine translation do simultaneous translation? *arXiv preprint arXiv:1606.02012*.

Chenhui Chu, Raj Dabre, and Sadao Kurohashi. 2017. An empirical comparison of domain adaptation methods for neural machine translation. In *Proceedings of the 55th Annual Meeting of the Association for Computational Linguistics (Volume 2: Short Papers)*, pages 385–391.

Sergey Edunov, Myle Ott, Michael Auli, and David Grangier. 2018. Understanding back-translation at scale. *arXiv preprint arXiv:1808.09381*.

Jiatao Gu, Graham Neubig, Kyunghyun Cho, and Victor O.K. Li. 2017. Learning to translate in real-time with neural machine translation. In *Proceedings of the 15th Conference of the European Chapter of the Association for Computational Linguistics: Volume 1, Long Papers*, pages 1053–1062, Valencia, Spain. Association for Computational Linguistics.

Junxian He, Jiatao Gu, Jiajun Shen, and Marc'Aurelio Ranzato. 2019. Revisiting self-training for neural sequence generation. *arXiv preprint arXiv:1909.13788*.

Marco Lui and Timothy Baldwin. 2012. langid. py: An off-the-shelf language identification tool. In *Proceedings of the ACL 2012 system demonstrations*, pages 25–30.

Minh-Thang Luong and Christopher D Manning. 2015. Stanford neural machine translation systems for spoken language domains. In *Proceedings of the 12th International Workshop on Spoken Language Translation: Evaluation Campaign*.

Mingbo Ma, Liang Huang, Hao Xiong, Renjie Zheng, Kaibo Liu, Baigong Zheng, Chuanqiang Zhang, Zhongjun He, Hairong Liu, Xing Li, et al. 2018. Stacl: Simultaneous translation with implicit anticipation and controllable latency using prefix-to-prefix framework. *arXiv preprint arXiv:1810.08398*.

Fandong Meng, Jianhao Yan, Yijin Liu, Yuan Gao, Xianfeng Zeng, Qinsong Zeng, Peng Li, Ming Chen, Jie Zhou, Sifan Liu, et al. 2020. Wechat neural machine translation systems for wmt20. *arXiv preprint arXiv:2010.00247*.

Robert C Moore and William Lewis. 2010. Intelligent selection of language model training data. In *Proceedings of the ACL 2010 conference short papers*, pages 220–224.

Nathan Ng, Kyra Yee, Alexei Baevski, Myle Ott, Michael Auli, and Sergey Edunov. 2019. Facebook fair's wmt19 news translation task submission. *arXiv preprint arXiv:1907.06616*.

Toan Q Nguyen and Julian Salazar. 2019. Transformers without tears: Improving the normalization of self-attention. *arXiv preprint arXiv:1910.05895*.

Kishore Papineni, Salim Roukos, Todd Ward, and Wei-Jing Zhu. 2002. Bleu: a method for automatic evaluation of machine translation. In *Proceedings of the 40th annual meeting of the Association for Computational Linguistics*, pages 311–318.

Rico Sennrich, Barry Haddow, and Alexandra Birch. 2015. Improving neural machine translation models with monolingual data. *arXiv preprint arXiv:1511.06709*.

Rico Sennrich, Barry Haddow, and Alexandra Birch. 2016. Neural machine translation of rare words with subword units. In *Proceedings of the 54th Annual Meeting of the Association for Computational Linguistics (Volume 1: Long Papers)*, pages 1715–1725, Berlin, Germany. Association for Computational Linguistics.

Meng Sun, Bojian Jiang, Hao Xiong, Zhongjun He, Hua Wu, and Haifeng Wang. 2019. Baidu neural machine translation systems for WMT19. In *Proceedings of the Fourth Conference on Machine Translation (Volume 2: Shared Task Papers, Day 1)*, pages 374–381, Florence, Italy. Association for Computational Linguistics.

Ashish Vaswani, Noam Shazeer, Niki Parmar, Jakob Uszkoreit, Llion Jones, Aidan N Gomez, Łukasz Kaiser, and Illia Polosukhin. 2017. Attention is all you need. *Advances in neural information processing systems*, 30.

Hongyu Wang, Shuming Ma, Li Dong, Shaohan Huang, Dongdong Zhang, and Furu Wei. 2022. Deepnet: Scaling transformers to 1,000 layers. *arXiv preprint arXiv:2203.00555*.

Qiang Wang, Bei Li, Tong Xiao, Jingbo Zhu, Changliang Li, Derek F. Wong, and Lidia S. Chao. 2019. Learning deep transformer models for machine translation. In *Proceedings of the 57th Annual Meeting of the Association for Computational Linguistics*, pages 1810–1822, Florence, Italy. Association for Computational Linguistics.

Ruiqing Zhang, Xiyang Wang, Chuanqiang Zhang, Zhongjun He, Hua Wu, Zhi Li, Haifeng Wang, Ying Chen, and Qinfei Li. 2021. Bstc: A large-scale chinese-english speech translation dataset. *arXiv preprint arXiv:2104.03575*.

Ruiqing Zhang, Chuanqiang Zhang, Zhongjun He, Hua Wu, and Haifeng Wang. 2020. Learning adaptive segmentation policy for simultaneous translation. In *Proceedings of the 2020 Conference on Empirical Methods in Natural Language Processing (EMNLP)*, pages 2280–2289.

A Appendix: Benchmarking comparison of paddle and fairseq

We subsampled the CWMT dataset to 2M size, set the same parameters and then trained 20 epochs with fairseq and paddle's Transformer respectively, and the experimental results are as Table 8.

Codebase	Architecture	BLEU
Fairseq	base	23.08
Paddle	base	**23.18**
Paddle	base+deepnorm	23.15
Paddle	12+6+deepnorm	23.12

Table 8: A benchmark comparison of Transformers with different architecture implemented using paddle and fairseq.

where "base" is the Transformer base; "deepnorm" means using the initialization and residual connection modification methods in DeepNet, and the default initialization is the same as fairseq. "12+6" means 12-layer encoder and 6-layer decoder, which is used in this paper.

We observed that the Paddle version of the Transformer performed slightly better the fairseq version. Aside from that, the Transformer base seems to outperform our implementation of deepnorm, probably due to the size of the dataset. We will test it on a larger dataset in the future.

Author Index